# SPONSORS TO THE EXHIBITION

**Control Data Corporation**

**Asian Art Museum Foundation of San Francisco**

**The Museum Society**

**The City and County of San Francisco**

**San Francisco-Shanghai Friendship City Committee**

**The San Francisco Foundation**

**Chevron Companies**

**Shaklee Corporation**

**CAAC (Civil Aviation Administration of China)**

**Wells Fargo Bank**

**Safeway Stores, Incorporated**

**The Society for Asian Art**

**California Arts Council**

Magic Mirror and Water Spurting Basin in Action.

# TREASURES FROM THE SHANGHAI MUSEUM 6,000 YEARS OF CHINESE ART

Edited by René-Yvon Lefebvre d'Argencé

*An exhibition organized by the Shanghai Museum and the Asian Art Museum of San Francisco for the following institutions in the United States and with their cooperation:*

Asian Art Museum of San Francisco
    May 4 – September 30, 1983

Field Museum of Natural History, Chicago
    November 1, 1983 – February 14, 1984

The Museum of Fine Arts, Houston
    March 16 – July 9, 1984

Smithsonian Institution, National Museum of Natural History / National Museum of Man, Washington, D.C.
    August 11 – November 30, 1984

# CREDITS

ORIGINAL ENTRIES: Staff of the Shanghai Museum
TRANSLATION: d'Argencé, Terese Tse Bartholomew, Patricia Berger, So Kam Ng, Clarence F. Shangraw
EDITING: d'Argencé, Jane Kallgren
PHOTOGRAPHY:
*Color Transparencies:* James Medley
*Black-and-white Negatives:*
   Numbers 17, 81 and 161: Shanghai Museum
   All Others: James Medley
*Prints:* Sharon Deveaux, Alison Taggart
LAYOUT AND DESIGN: d'Argencé, Cecelia Levin
COVER CALLIGRAPHY: Zheng Wei
MAP: d'Argencé, Terese Tse Bartholomew, Clarence F. Shangraw
CHRONOLOGY: d'Argencé, Patricia Berger, Clarence F. Shangraw
SELECTED BIBLIOGRAPHY: d'Argencé, Patricia Berger, Clarence F. Shangraw
MANUSCRIPT: Dorothy Franks, Jane Kallgren

**The publication of this catalogue was made possible by a grant from the California Arts Council.**

# TABLE OF CONTENTS

# MESSAGE 致　　词

《上海博物馆珍藏——六千年的中国艺术展览》一九八三年五月在旧金山亚洲艺术博物馆揭幕了。这是上海和旧金山两个城市之间重要的文化交流，也是中美两国人民友好关系的体现。我代表上海市人民政府和上海人民热烈祝贺展览会的开幕。

中美两国人民有着传统的深厚的友谊。中美建交之后，上海市同旧金山市于一九八○年一月结成了友好城市，这是中美两国间建立的第一对友好城市。我们高兴地看到，在过去三年中，由于双方的共同努力，两市的各种形式的友好交流得到了令人满意的发展。我相信，这次中国珍贵文物在美的展出，可以使旧金山、芝加哥、休斯敦和华盛顿等地的市民进一步了解光辉灿烂的中国古代文化，必将增进中美两国人民的友谊。

中华人民共和国同美利坚合众国两国关系的发展，符合两国人民的利益，也有利于维护世界的和平。我们希望中美两国关系在中美建交公报的原则基础上进一步发展，上海和旧金山两市的友好关系不断增进。

我愿就此机会向美国东道主以及各位观众致以良好的祝愿，热烈的问候。

上　海　市　长　　汪道涵

"TREASURES FROM THE SHANGHAI MUSEUM—6,000 YEARS OF CHINESE ART" is going to be inaugurated in May of 1983 in the Asian Art Museum of San Francisco. The exhibition, which demonstrates the friendly relations between the Chinese and American peoples, is an important item in the cultural exchanges between Shanghai and San Francisco. On behalf of the Municipal People's Government and the people of Shanghai, I would like to extend my warm congratulations on its opening.

There exists a profound traditional friendship between the Chinese and American peoples. Shanghai and San Francisco forged the friendship city ties in January, 1980, one year after the establishment of diplomatic relations between the People's Republic of China and the United States of America. They are the first pair of friendship cities ever set up between the two countries. It is gratifying to note that, thanks to our mutual efforts, satisfactory progress has been registered in the friendly interchanges of various forms between the two cities. I believe that the exhibition will give a good opportunity to the citizens of San Francisco, Chicago, Houston and Washington to know better the splendid ancient culture of China, thus enhancing the friendship between the two peoples.

The development of the relations between the People's Republic of China and the United States of America is in the interests of the two peoples and advantageous to the maintaining of world peace. It is my hope that the relations between the two countries would be further promoted on the basis of the principles enunciated in the Joint Communique on the Establishment of Diplomatic Relations between the People's Republic of China and the United States of America and that the amicable relationship between Shanghai and San Francisco be continuously strengthened.

Wang Daohan
Mayor of Shanghai

In late 1979, the Sister City relationship between San Francisco and Shanghai was established. Approved at the highest levels of the government of the People's Republic of China, this was the first such relationship between the People's Republic and the United States. This friendly association of two great cities, in the three years of its existence, has resulted in many exciting programs of mutual benefit. The bonds of friendship and trade have been greatly strengthened.

As Mayor, through the San Francisco-Shanghai Friendship Committee, I have sought, and will continue to seek, new ways to bring our two cities, our two cultures, together. I am honored that Shanghai has offered these treasures to us as a testament to our friendship. Having visited the Shanghai Museum, I can appreciate the extraordinary work that was involved in selecting the objects and organizing this superb presentation. I congratulate the Asian Art Commission and its staff for the successful exhibition of these treasures for San Francisco and for their continuing responsibility for the national tour.

I believe that "Treasures from the Shanghai Museum: 6,000 Years of Chinese Art" will be a great contribution to the continuing effort our two countries are making to build new bridges of understanding and respect. I truly hope one day the bridges between our two cities and nations will shrink the vast Pacific into a gentle river.

Warmest Regards,

Dianne Feinstein
Mayor of San Francisco

一九七九年末，经过中华人民共和国最高阶层政府的同意，上海市与旧金山缔结为姊妹城市。此乃中美双方两城市间结为姊妹城的首次。缔交三年以来，两城市间展开许多有趣的互惠活动，双方的友谊及商务活动也因此更为增强。

身为市长，透过旧金山及上海友谊委员会，我一直不断的致力於寻求两城市及中美两文化交流，结合的新途径。此次上海市以提供上海市藏中国宝贵文物在旧金山展览做为两市友谊的见证，使我倍感荣幸。自参观上海博物馆后，我深能了解此次选择展品及筹备展出工作的繁重。我恭贺亚洲美术委员会及其工作人员此次文物展览在旧金山展出成功，并鼓励他们继续为展览在其他城市展出成功而努力。

我相信＂六千年的中国艺术展览＂为我们两国之间的了解和尊敬建立了更新的桥梁。我深切希望我们两市和两国之间的友谊桥梁能将浩瀚的太平洋缩短为一条缓缓的溪流。

旧金山市长　　黛安·范士丹

## FOREWORD AND ACKNOWLEDGEMENTS

Conceived specifically for the United States, this exhibition breaks new ground in several other respects.

It is much wider in scope than any other exhibition sent from China to this country since it offers to the American public an overall view of the development of Chinese art from the Neolithic period to the present. The volume, nature and quality of what has been accomplished in China in the fields of archaeology and art history during the past thirty years or so makes it necessary for all amateurs of Chinese art to reassess many of the notions, theories and judgements that were more or less taken for granted until recently.

Where ancient China is concerned, such reassessment has already been greatly facilitated by two major traveling exhibitions. However, the achievements of the Chinese archaeologists, art historians and museum curators of this generation are by no means restricted to the early periods. The harvest has been considerable for the later dynasties as well, and the time has come to take a bird's-eye view which furnishes students, collectors and amateurs alike with the main trends in the development of the oldest living culture in the world. Thus, in our selection emphasis has been placed on items which bring out some of the most significant moments in the history of Chinese art.

Such an ambitious project would not have seen the light without the full cooperation of the Shanghai Museum, which is known for the vastness and excellence of its holdings, as well as for its dynamism and far-sightedness. All the complex negotiations that are inherent in organizing an international exhibition of this magnitude were conducted in a climate of friendship, perhaps best exemplified by the procedure adopted in the preparation of this catalogue.

For what appears to be the first time in the history of cultural exchange between China and the United States, the catalogue of a major exhibition is the fruit of a dialogue between the two parties. Most of the photographs of the exhibits were taken in Shanghai by the Asian Art Museum staff photographer, whose task was greatly helped by a special "trial" exhibition which the Shanghai Museum set up essentially for that purpose. Prepared in Chinese by the staff of the Shanghai Museum, the text of the introductory essays and of the entries was translated and annotated by the staff of the Asian Art Museum. Realizing that this was a unique opportunity for our visitors and readers to have direct access to Chinese sources and insight and to benefit from the enlightening and eloquent commentaries of our colleagues in Shanghai, we attempted in our translation to preserve as much of the original flavor of the Chinese text as possible. We wanted our readers to partake in a terminology and an imagery which are integral parts of the Chinese approach to art appreciation.

All large international exhibitions require much effort, expertise, dedication and support on the part of many patrons, contributors and sponsors. This one originated more than three years ago when Mayor Feinstein invited Vice Mayor Zhao Xingzhi to San Francisco to celebrate the establishment of a sister city relationship between Shanghai and San Francisco. Both Mayors gave their unreserved support to the idea of planning a major exchange between the museums of their respective cities, and this enthusiastic support has played a decisive role in the realization of the project.

On the Chinese side, the expression of our deepest gratitude also goes to the Honorable Wang Daohan, Mayor of Shanghai; Mr. Lin Deming, Deputy Director, Shanghai Municipal Office of Foreign Affairs; Mr. Guo Laowei, Chief of the Foreign Affairs Section, State Administrative Bureau of Museums and Archaeological Data, in Beijing; Mr. Fang Xing, Bureau Chief, Cultural Bureau, City of Shanghai; Mr. Li Shoupao, Vice President, Shanghai People's Friendship Association; His Excellency Chai Zemin, Ambassador of the People's Republic of China; and the Honorable Hu Dingyi and Xie Heng, respectively Consul General and Cultural Consul of the People's Republic of China in San Francisco, for their generous patronage and valuable advice.

On the American side, Mayor Feinstein's enthusiasm was echoed by her special assistant Mr. Peter Henschel and her San Francisco-Shanghai Friendship City Committee, headed by Mr. Gordon Lau. The Asian Art Commission under the leadership of Mrs. Brayton Wilbur, Jr. and its Shanghai Exhibition Planning Committee, chaired by Mr. Alexander D. Calhoun, have successfully dealt with all organizational and financial issues. In all budgetary and fund raising matters, the experience, savoir faire and sheer dedication of Mr. James M. Gerstley, Vice Chairman-Treasurer of the Asian Art Museum Foundation of San Francisco, have been invaluable.

A list of our national and local sponsors appears at the beginning of this catalogue, and this list will no doubt be augmented as the exhibition travels to other cities in the United States. We are profoundly grateful to all these sponsors for making the exhibition possible. National and principal support came from Control Data Corporation, whose grant ranks among the most important contributions ever made by a corporation or governmental agency for a project of this kind. We are also most grateful to the Federal Council on the Arts and Humanities for granting indemnity to the exhibition and to the California Arts Council for a generous grant in connection with the publication of this catalogue.

We are also deeply grateful to our friends and colleagues Dr. Lorin I. Nevling, Jr., Director, Field Museum of Natural History; Dr. Peter Marzio, Director, The Museum of Fine Arts, Houston; Mr. Paul N. Perrot, Assistant Secretary for Museum Programs, Smithsonian Institution, and Dr. Richard S. Fiske, Director, National Museum of Natural History/ National Museum of Man, for their cooperation and enthusiastic support of the exhibition.

Aided during the initial stage of planning by Lyndel King, Director of the University of Minnesota Gallery, and former Director, Exhibitions and Museum Programs, Control Data Arts, the staff of the Asian Art Museum has spared no effort in the preparation of the exhibition and of this catalogue. We wish to thank in particular John B. Dowty, Assistant Director, Administration; Jack Foss, Registrar; Lorrie Bunker, Public

Relations Director; Clarence F. Shangraw, Senior Curator, who designed the display for San Francisco and supervised its installation; and Conservator Roger D. Broussal, who planned with loving care for the physical welfare of the exhibits. Where the catalogue is concerned, I am especially indebted to James Medley, our staff photographer, as well as to Terese Tse Bartholomew, Curator of Indian Art; Cecelia Levin, Curator of Education, and Jane Kallgren, Secretary to the Director, whose linguistic, designing and editing talents have been of tremendous help in the preparation of this publication.

Finally, we are deeply appreciative of the confidence Mr. Shen Zhiyu, Director of the Shanghai Museum, and his staff have placed in us. The close relationship between our museums has raised international cooperation to new heights.

René-Yvon Lefebvre d'Argencé
Director and Chief Curator
Asian Art Museum of San Francisco

# INTRODUCTION TO THE EXHIBITION

Since the establishment of diplomatic relations between the People's Republic of China and the United States of America, constantly increasing contacts between the people of the two countries have greatly contributed to mutual understanding and friendship. In January 1980, the cities of Shanghai and San Francisco became Sister Cities, and at the request of the Asian Art Museum of San Francisco, the Shanghai Museum began to organize this special exhibition to travel in the United States. We hope that, through the cooperation of our American museum colleagues, it will advance cultural exchanges between the people of our two countries.

This comprehensive exhibition of Chinese art covers over 6,000 years and comprises 232 objects, which may be grouped into the following five categories: artifacts excavated in Shanghai, bronze vessels, pottery and porcelain, paintings and applied arts and crafts. These categories will serve as the framework of this brief introduction to the archaeological activity in Shanghai and to the origin and evolution of each class of objects.

I. Archaeological Materials Excavated in Shanghai

Archaeological work is one of the important programs of the Shanghai Museum. Only one ancient cultural site was discovered in Shanghai prior to Liberation, but we have now found 25 sites dating from the Neolithic to the Chunqiu and Warring States periods. We have also excavated and inventoried more than two hundred tombs dating from the late Neolithic period to the Ming dynasty, thus unearthing over three thousand artifacts. These discoveries have provided a great deal of material for scientific research on the geological formation of the Shanghai area and the political, economic and cultural conditions of successive dynasties.

In 1960 we found an ancient cultural site in the central part of Shanghai City at the remains of the shoreline, known as the Zhugang ("Bamboo Ridge"). We called it the Maqiao site. The lower stratum of the site, which belongs to the late neolithic Liangzhu culture,[1] yielded *ding* vessels with T-shaped legs, eared *hu, dou* with "bamboo joint" handles, *gui* with hollow, lobed legs, *he* with three solid legs, etc. The shells that

form the vestiges of the shoreline have been subjected to carbon 14 testing which dated them to 5,680 plus or minus 180 years ago, proving that the so-called "Bamboo Ridge" was formed 5,000 years ago and that the people of the Liangzhu culture occupied the ridge over 4,000 years ago. This shows that 5,000 or 6,000 years ago the area west of the Bamboo Ridge was already alluvial land.

However, the objects excavated from the Maqiao site are not the oldest cultural remains in Shanghai. The earliest are from the Songze site[2] in Qingpu County to the west of the Bamboo Ridge, which has three ancient cultural strata. The lowest stratum, which is characterized by tongue-shaped stone axes with perforations, round-bottomed *fu* pots with flanged waists and red-slipped burnished pottery *dou*, belongs to the Majiabang neolithic culture of the Taihu region. Carbon 14 tests performed on pieces of charcoal found in association with these items gave a dating of 5,980 plus or minus 140 years ago.

Thanks to the results of our many years of archaeological work, we now know that the sequence of ancient cultures in the Shanghai area is as follows: Majiabang culture, Songze culture, Liangzhu culture, Maqiao type and Qijiadun type, which is contemporaneous with the Chunqiu to Warring States periods.

## II. Bronze Vessels

The Chinese Bronze Age refers primarily to the Shang, Western Zhou, Chunqiu and Warring States periods. It produced tools, weapons, cooking, food, wine and water vessels, musical instruments and ornaments for horses and chariots. Shapes are varied; decoration is refined and elegant. In 1959 at Erlitou in Yanshi, Henan, an important site of the early Shang dynasty was discovered and yielded bronze artifacts such as knives, spearheads, *jue* vessels and *ling* bells. The cultural layer and vestiges place Erlitou later than the Henan Longshan culture and earlier than the Erligang culture[3] of Zhengzhou. The strata can be divided into four phases, and, according to carbon 14 results, the dates of the remains of the first phase correspond to those of the Xia dynasty (21st–16th century B.C.). This is of considerable significance to the study of the origins of Shang culture and the research on Xia culture. So far, Chinese scholars have not yet reached a conclusion as to whether the bronze vessels unearthed from the third stratum of Erlitou belong to the culture of the Xia dynasty or to the early Shang culture. However, it has been clearly established that the bronze vessels of the Erligang culture (16th–14th century B.C.) are earlier than the Yinxu culture of Xiaotun at Anyang.

The bronze vessels of the middle and late Shang and early Western Zhou (14th–10th century B.C.)[4] represent a climax in the bronze industry of the slave society. Their workmanship is superb; their shapes are dignified and diversified. Their magnificent ornamentation is mainly based on animal mask decoration, *kui* dragon, phoenix and various other animal motifs, as well as geometric patterns. In late Shang, bronze is already cast on to meteoric iron in making weapons. However, inscriptions remain relatively short. From the middle of Western Zhou to early Chunqiu[5] (10th–latter half of the 6th century B.C.), the style tends toward simplification, with decoration changing from careful and precise to coarse and loose, but lengthy inscriptions become more numerous. At this time, there is also an increase in utensils made for the feudal states and a rapid decrease in those made for the royal family and its officials. To a certain degree, this reflects the decline of the royal house as well as a political situation where big states are contending for hegemony.

The period from middle and late Chunqiu to the Warring States[6] (latter half of the 6th century–221 B.C.) is one of transition from a slave to a feudal society. Bronze vessels of the time are no longer monopolized by slave-owning aristocrats, but begin to be used by the emergent landlord class. Along with the expansion of production and the extensive development of interchange, many cities appear in the feudal states, and bronze casting reaches another pinnacle, as exemplified by the large assemblage of bells[7] excavated from the tomb of the Marquis of Zeng in Leigudun, Sui County,[8] Hubei, a region where the lost-wax casting technique was extraordinarily advanced. This is a period of innovative workmanship and precise, splendid decoration, with lively animal motifs as well as close-knit, intricate geometric patterns. Some are stamped into continuous ornamental schemes; some are hunting, battle and banquet scenes carved in fine lines and stippled. In addition, there are inlaid gold and silver utensils with designs in gold, silver, solid copper and jade.

During the Qin and Han dynasties, the products of the lacquer, ceramic and cast-iron industries largely replace bronze vessels. Bronze in general has already started to decline in the Central Plain where it is no longer emblematic of the civilization of the period, even though it continues to be on the ascendant in the bordering regions. This is also a time of widespread innovations in casting techniques, such as the appearance of gilded vessels. More specifically, the manufacture of bronze mirrors, which cannot be replaced functionally by lacquer objects, continues to develop all over the country.[9]

### III. Pottery and Porcelain

China has a long history of ceramic technology, which in ancient times was an important aspect of the development of agriculture and handicrafts. In both the Yellow and Yangzi river basins, our archaeologists have unearthed pottery vessels that predate the Yangshao culture.[10] By the time of the Shang dynasty slave society, white pottery made from kaolin and proto-porcelain vessels with man-made glazes are already in use. Thereafter, as production levels rise and the feudal system persists, the Han dynasty sees the successful creation of lead, black and white glazes and the appearance of mature celadons. By the 4th century B.C. there is considerable development in such wares in the southeastern region[11] and striking progress in the luminosity of porcelain glazes. By Tang times, bichromatic glazes appear at the Lushan kiln and the Jia County kiln in Henan and underglaze painting at the Changsha kiln in Hunan—both important technological breakthroughs—while the high degree of quality reached in the art of modeling three-color potteries is even more remarkable.[12] By the middle of the Tang, Chinese porcelains are already sold abroad, and China becomes famous throughout the world as the "porcelain country."

The important categories of Chinese porcelains are celadons, white wares and polychromes. During the Tang dynasty, the Yue kilns[13] are the most famous for celadons, and the Xing kilns,[14] the site of which has now been discovered at Qicun, Lincheng, in Hebei, are the most famous for white porcelains.

The Song and Yuan dynasties make important contributions in porcelain technology. The porcelain kilns of the Northern and Southern Song are distributed all over the north, east and south of China. The *qingbai* glazes,[15] which flourish in various southern kilns, and the ''kiln transmutations'' of the Jun kilns[16] in Henan are gratifying innovations. At that time, folk kilns such as those of Cizhou[17] in the north invent the technique of incising decoration through multi-layered slips, thus initiating a fresh and lively folk style.

The biggest contribution of Yuan ceramic technology is underglaze painting.[18] Mature underglaze blue and the successful creation of underglaze red best exemplify the important accomplishments in firing techniques reached during that dynasty.

The Ming and Qing dynasties are a colorful period in the history of Chinese ceramics. The appearance of monochrome glazes, as well as *doucai*[19] and *wucai*[20] decoration during the Ming and *fencai*[21] and *falang cai*[22] decoration during the Qing, give a dazzlingly brilliant aspect to porcelains, and, as a result, the ceramic industry of Jingdezhen becomes world famous.

## IV. Paintings

Chinese painting has a long history, a unique artistic approach and a rigid theoretical background. In the more than 800 years from the Western and Eastern Han through the early Tang, painting subjects were, for the most part, historical narratives. Thereafter, Buddhism was propagated in China. Religious art practically becomes the mainstream, but continues to center on figure painting—the depiction of natural scenery and of birds and animals still serving only as a foil. After the mid-Tang, landscape painting and bird-and-flower painting gradually develop, while folk paintings, such as Buddhist effigies, add their own lustre. Their fluid lines and simple, bold colors remain a brilliant page in the history of Chinese painting. By the time of the Five Dynasties and the Northern and Southern Song, academic painting flourishes, and many famous artists, academic and non-academic, appear. Landscape painting and bird-and-flower painting make even greater artistic progress. Whether historical narratives or folk figure paintings, they are especially lively and realistic. During the Yuan, a stylistic change takes place, literati painting develops greatly and is the source of a deep and far-reaching influence on the various schools of painting during the Ming and Qing. While some literati emphasize individual expression, others pursue the spirit of the brush and ink or again devote themselves to imitation of antiquity. They thus form numerous local schools in the north and south, break new stylistic ground and create a rich, colorful technical springboard for Ming and Qing painting.

After 1840, national consciousness and patriotism prompt some painters to seek energetically a path through the fine traditions of ''national'' art. They stress painting from nature and use calligraphic brushwork to counteract sentimentality, thus enabling literati painting to make new progress in brush and ink techniques.

## V. Applied Arts and Crafts

The term ''applied arts and crafts'' refers to the various categories of valuable, functional and decorative art objects, other than bronze vessels and pottery or porcelain. These objects include jade, lacquer, cloisonné and carved bamboo, wood, ivory, rhinoceros horn, jadeite, carnelian, etc.

In China the technique of jade carving originates with the boring of stone objects, which may be traced to the late phase of the Paleolithic period when the Upper Cave Man perforated pieces of gravel as ornaments. Thus, a technique of boring holes through stones lays a firm foundation for subsequent jade carving technique. Jade ornaments, such as the *huang*[23] and the *jue*, have been discovered throughout China in burials of neolithic date. A ritual object more than 4,000 years old of the Liangzhu culture, the jade *cong* displayed in this exhibition,[24] has been bored from both ends through a length of 39.3 centimeters. Thereafter, the carving technique consistently improves throughout the ages. It can be divided into three categories: low relief, openwork and carving in the round, all highly treasured by rulers throughout history. Carved jades were used as objects of display, personal ornaments, weapons and as ritual objects in court ceremonies, sacrifices and funerary rites.

Evidence that lacquer was used over 6,000 years ago has been provided by archaeological materials from Hemudu in Zhejiang. In addition, fragments of an exquisitely decorated lacquerware of the late Shang period have been discovered at Taixicun in Gaocheng, Hebei. By the Warring States, Qin and Han periods, lacquer is highly developed, as can be seen in the large number of objects as shiny as new unearthed at such places as Jiangling and Yunmeng in Hubei and Changsha in Hunan dating from this period. Thereafter, many methods of manufacture were developed, such as carving, inlaying with colored lacquer, painting with gold, polychrome painting and mother-of-pearl inlay. Carved lacquers are first made in the Tang dynasty, while Song and Yuan are transitional periods. Stylistically straightforward, Ming carved lacquers display a well-rounded, seasoned cutting method and a smooth polish—the products of the Guoyuan factory in Beijing are particularly famous. Qing carving remains fine, but tends toward stylistic over-elaboration.

Among the exhibits, there are examples of cloisonné enamels on a copper body from both the Ming and Qing.[25] The earliest extant cloisonnés are those handed down from the Ming Xuande reign (1426–1435), but the Ming Jingtai period (1450–1456) is the time when they become widely popular, and cloisonnés are generally referred to as "Jingtai blues."[26] During the Qing dynasty a great quantity of such wares was already being exported abroad. The manufacturing process consists of hammering the body, attaching the *cloisons*, filling them with enamels, baking the enamels, polishing and gilding.

I hope that this brief introduction to archaeological activities in Shanghai and to the origin and evolution of each category of exhibit will be of some assistance to the visitors to the exhibition.

Shen Zhiyu
Director
Shanghai Museum

( 1)   See Colorplates I and II; Figures 6 and 8.
( 2)   See Figures 1–4.
( 3)   See Colorplate V; Figures 13 and 15.
( 4)   See Colorplates VI–X; Figures 16–18, 21–23, 26, 27 and 29–31.
( 5)   See Colorplates XI–XII; Figures 34–38.
( 6)   See Figures 40–47.
( 7)   Sixty-five of them.
( 8)   See *The Tomb of Marquis Yi of the Zeng State at Sui County,* Hubei Provincial Museum, Wenwu Publishers, Beijing, 1980.
( 9)   See Colorplate XIV and Figure 52.
(10)   See Colorplate II.
(11)   See Figure 46.
(12)   See Colorplate XXII; Figures 65, 67, 68 and 70.
(13)   See Figure 74.
(14)   See Figure 73.
(15)   Also known as *yingqing* ("shadowy blue").
(16)   See Figure 80.
(17)   See Colorplate XXVIII and Figure 88.
(18)   See Figure 93.
(19)   "Opposite or contrasted colors": a type of decoration combining underglaze blue outline and overglaze enamels.
(20)   See Colorplate XXXVII.
(21)   See Figure 145.
(22)   Also known in the West as *famille rose.*
(23)   See Figure 47.
(24)   See Colorplate I.
(25)   See Figures 116 and 147.
(26)   景泰蓝 .

# INTRODUCTION TO
# THE SHANGHAI MUSEUM

Devoted to the fine arts of China, the Shanghai Museum was established after the Liberation and formally opened its doors to the public on December 21, 1952.

Our basic displays are arranged by subject matter and chronologically. To date we have set up displays of bronzes, ceramics and paintings with exhibits reflecting the special characteristics of the museum and serving as a general introduction to the development of these categories.

The Bronze Galleries include over six hundred items divided into four sections. The first section consists of objects and rubbings of engraved inscriptions which give a brief introduction to the Shang and Zhou slave society and explain the social background of bronze production. Focusing on bronze casting technology, the second section deals with mining and smelting and displays demonstration models which illustrate the technical processes of making ceramic molds and alloys. This section also displays a quantitative analysis of the alloy ratios used in Shang and Zhou wine vessels, cooking vessels and weapons and Han and Tang bronze mirrors, thus showing how the alloy ratios of bronze artifacts varied with their respective usage. In addition, by explaining why and how the magic mirror works,[1] this second section demonstrates the high technological level reached by ancient bronze casters. The third display section is the focal point of the entire bronze exhibition. It features fine bronzes representative of the Shang and Zhou dynasties and includes wine vessels, food vessels, cooking vessels, water vessels and musical instruments.[2] These objects systematically introduce each stage of development in Chinese bronze craftsmanship and reflect the brilliant accomplishments of China's ancient material culture. The fourth section displays bronzes of the minorities, such as the Baiyue,[3] the Ba,[4] the Dian[5] and the Xiongnu.[6] These show how the bronzes of the ancient minorities also played a prominent role in cultural exchanges and the integration of a national culture. They formed an important part of the art of the Chinese Bronze Age.

The Ceramic Galleries—with over six hundred objects ranging from the Yangshao painted pottery of the primitive society to the exquisite ceramics of our times—give a succinct introduction to the history of China's ceramic development. The first section includes specimens of early hand-built pottery and painted pottery made at Banpo, Miaodigou,[7] Majiayao,[8] Banshan and Machang, as well as ceramics excavated from Songze in Shanghai's Qingpu County.[9] These introduce "the birth of pottery and the ceramic technology of the primitive society." Highlighted by a Shang dynasty green-glazed *zun* with bowstring decoration, Qin dynasty soldier and horse figures, a small black-glazed jar excavated from an Eastern Han tomb and Wei-Jin celadons, the second section introduces "the technical development of pottery, the appearance of the proto-porcelain and the systematic formation of celadon in the southeastern region of China." The third section, which includes Tang three-color ware,[10] Yue celadons,[11] two-color Jiaxian ware[12] and Changsha underglaze painted ware, displays "the rich and colorful ceramics of the Sui, Tang and Five Dynasties periods." The fourth section displays Jingdezhen Qingbai ware, Ding white-glazed ware, Longchuan and Yaozhou celadons and Cizhou-type Dengfeng, Dangyangyu and Pacun black-on-white decorated wares.[13] There are also precious porcelains from the five great Song kilns—Guan, Ge, Ru, Jun and Ding[14]—which as a group reveal the flourishing development of ceramics during the two Song periods. The fifth section stresses "the new accomplishments of the ceramic art at Jingdezhen during the Yuan, Ming and Qing dynasties." Besides these, there are also several sections such as those of "Yuan, Ming and Qing ceramics produced outside of Jingdezhen" and "export ceramics."

This display system offers an altogether fresh didactic approach. For example, porcelain is one of China's outstanding discoveries, but there is still debate throughout the world as to when exactly it was first made. Even today the scientific difference between pottery and porcelain remains a topic of research. The display uses actual objects and accessory charts to clarify the differences between the two. At the same time, it shows that the Shang already created primitive porcelain and that celadons gradually reached a stage of maturity during the period from the Warring States to the Han. "Green in the south, white in the north,"[15] a time-honored saying in ceramic circles, means that in ancient times celadons prevailed in the south and white wares in the north. However, our display contains early Eastern Han white wares excavated from southern China's Hunan Province. These provide scholars with important research material in connection with the origin of white wares. Again, ceramic history previously treated the products of the Deqing kilns of the Eastern Jin dynasty[16] as the earliest examples of black-glazed ware, but this museum has on exhibition a small black-glazed jar excavated from an Eastern Han tomb at Zhenjiang and dated the 13th year of Yongyuan (101 A.D.). This is, therefore, the earliest reliable black-glazed object we have up to now with an absolute date and is as such an important piece of evidence in the creation of black glazes.

The Painting Galleries illustrate a systematic outline of the development of Chinese painting over more than four thousand years. The layout intersperses discussions on specific topics and introductions to schools while following the chronological order and illustrating each phase in the development of painting. This brings forth the general characteristics and styles of each period, as well as a profile of each school.

To explain the development of painting, we use essentially reproductions for the Tang and pre-Tang periods and originals starting from the Song dynasty. There are patterns on painted pottery from China's primitive society,[17] traces of decorative patterns known as "flowery dirt"[18] that are found impressed on wooden objects excavated from slave society tombs, reproductions of paintings on silk of the late Warring States and early Western Han, as well as of murals and handscrolls representative of the Han to Tang dynasties. They vividly portray the social life of these periods and the high level attained in figures, landscapes and "ruled line"[19] paintings.

The bulk of the painting display is post-Tang and consists of over one hundred twenty pieces which occupy three large galleries: one for the Song and Yuan dynasties, another for the Ming and Qing dynasties and the last for modern times. This chronological display brings to light the two main currents in Chinese painting, namely, the Academic and Literati schools. The Ming-Qing section is arranged according to different regional schools, such as those of Zhejiang, Jiangsu, Songjiang, Nanjing, Anhui and Yangzhou. Special emphasis is placed on the Ming dynasty Wu school of Suzhou,[20] the Zhe school of Zhejiang,[21] the Songjiang school[22] led by Dong Qichang and its Taicang[23] and Yushan[24] branches, the Qing dynasty Jinling school of Nanjing,[25] the Xin'an school of Anhui,[26] and the Jiangxi[27] and Yangzhou[28] schools. Each school raised its own banner in the painting arena with its own unique artistic style. The final display exhibits outstanding works by modern painters—Zhao Zhiqian, Wu Changshuo,[29] Ren Bonian,[30] Xugu,[31] Chen Hengke,[32] Qi Baishi,[33] etc.

The Shanghai Museum houses over one hundred four thousand objects of every type. The collections' strengths are in bronzes, ceramics, calligraphy and painting. Among other comprehensive collections are imperial signets and seals, coins and all kinds of artifacts. Most of the objects in the museum's collection were purchased. Others were donated by the masses or provided by friendly museums in other provinces and cities. Some were excavated by this museum.

The Shanghai Museum pays serious attention to education. Each year the museum organizes numerous groups of people who come to the museum to view and study. In order to strengthen ties with those who enjoy museum work, the museum also organized the "Friends of the Shanghai Museum" including professors, students, specialists, collectors, traditional style painters and designers. The museum occasionally makes special arrangements for them to see the city's Cultural Properties, to view the museum's new acquisitions, as well as important illustrated catalogues of foreign objects. In order to take advantage of the skills of outside specialists, the museum invited seven people to be "Consultants to the Scientific and Technological Laboratory for the Protection of the Shanghai Museum's Cultural Properties," among them professors from Fudan University, directors and engineers from the Pesticide Research Institute, the Pharmaceutical Institute, the Paint Research Institute, the Industrial Sanitation Research Institute and the

Laser Beam Technological Research Institute. All these enthusiastic specialists of the protection of cultural properties have made definite contributions to the conservation of this museum's collections.

Li Junjie
Administrator
Shanghai Museum

( 1)   See Colorplate XIV.
( 2)   See Colorplates V and VII–XIII; Figures 13, 15–18, 21, 26, 27, 29–31, 34–36, and 39–43.
( 3)   百越, southern and southeastern minorities of ancient China.
( 4)   巴族, minorities of Sichuan in ancient China.
( 5)   滇族, minorities of Yunnan Province.
( 6)   匈奴族, the Huns, an ancient nationality in northern China.
( 7)   The Miaodigou site revealed the second major localized painted pottery style in the Central Plain and partly overlapped with the Yangshao Banpo type cultures.
( 8)   The Majiayao culture was distributed throughout the Gansu and Qinghai regions. It was later than the Yangshao culture (of the Central Plain). It has provided crucial materials for the study of painted pottery styles in the northwest region.
( 9)   See Figures 1–4.
(10)   See Colorplate XXII; Figures 65, 67, 68 and 70.
(11)   See Figure 74.
(12)   See Figure 72.
(13)   See Figure 88.
(14)   See Colorplates XXIII and XXIV; Figures 78, 80, 82 and 83.
(15)   *Zhongguo Taoci Shi (History of Chinese Ceramics)*, Beijing, Cultural Press, 1982, p. 191.
(16)   The kiln site is in Deqing County, Zhejiang. See *ibid.*, p. 144.
(17)   See Colorplate II.
(18)   花土.
(19)   See Figure 133.
(20)   See Figures 97 and 98.
(21)   See Figures 103 and 104.
(22)   See Colorplate XXXV.
(23)   See Figures 122 and 123.
(24)   See Figure 124.
(25)   See Figure 132.
(26)   See Figure 128.
(27)   See Figure 130.
(28)   See Figures 136–139.
(29)   See Figure 156.
(30)   See Figure 141.
(31)   See Figure 140.
(32)   1876–1923. See also Catalogue number 105, footnote (13) and Catalogue number 157, footnote (4).
(33)   See Colorplate LII.

# 6,000 YEARS OF CHINESE ART

China is famous throughout the world for its ancient civilization. Approximately 6,000 years ago, ancestors of the Chinese people already used pictographic symbols to record events and, through their labor, had already produced in large areas of the Yellow and Yangzi River basins material and spiritual riches reflecting a high degree of intelligence.

Since the 1950's, Shanghai has developed its field archaeology in a major way. Investigations and excavations have taken place one after another in some twenty areas, such as Maqiao in Shanghai County; Songze, Guoyuancun and Fuquanshan in Qingpu County; Guangfulin and Tangmiaocun in Songjiang County; Zhelin in Fengxian County; Qijiadun, Chashan and Tinglin in Jinshan County. Among these, the excavations of Songze in Qingpu and Maqiao in Shanghai County have provided a wealth of material of the utmost importance for the study of the ancient culture of the southeastern area. It proves that the area of the lower Yangzi was not developed later than the Yellow River basin. From early on, it was inhabited by aboriginal clans and tribes who together formed a huge cultural system. The Majiabang, Songze and Liangzhu cultures, which constitute a chronological sequence in Shanghai, are connected with the Hemudu culture of the Ningshao Plain on the south shore of the Bay of Hangzhou, as well as with relics of the Beiyinyangying type in the Yangzi and Huai River basins, and with the Dawenkou culture of the lower reaches of the Yellow River.

This cultural system developed concurrently with the Yangshao, Majiayao and Longshan cultures of the middle and upper reaches of the Yellow River. Each of these cultures had its own system, but they also influenced one another over the broad expanse of China's territory. Different local economic conditions caused them to branch out into various directions. Among the objects shown in this exhibition, the grey pottery pig-shaped *yi* (Figure 2), the grey pottery *dou* (Figure 1) and the black pottery openwork *hu* with two walls (Figure 4) were excavated in Shanghai and are typical of the southeastern cultural system. The revolving flower pattern in openwork (Figure 4) is characteristic of the south. It illustrates an advanced form of the openwork technique inherited from the Hemudu and Majiabang cultures as it tends toward a continuous design. The exquisite black pottery three-legged *he* with lid (Figure 6) is typical of the Liangzhu culture.

About 2000 B.C. at the time of the Xia dynasty, as it is called in history, or the pre-Shang dynasty, China entered the Bronze Age. A primitive communal system was gradually superseded by the slave system. The Xia area of activity was in present-day southern Shanxi and western Henan. The so-called "Erlitou type culture," so far exemplified by discoveries made in Yucun, Dengfeng; Luodamiao, Zhengzhou; Donggan'gou, Luoyang; and Erlitou, Yanshi in Henan Province, took place between the Longshan culture and early Shang. It existed prior to the Erligang phase, Zhengzhou, of the early Shang, and this is why Chinese archaeologists consider that it belongs to the Xia dynasty culture.

Bronze tools, weapons and containers, such as knives,[1] bells,[2] arrowheads and *jue* (tripods),[3] have been excavated in the late stratum of the Erlitou site. At the same time, a bronze foundry site yielded pottery molds, bronze slag and fragments of crucibles. While some vestiges and relics from the late stratum of Erlitou, such as round-bottomed vessels, pottery kilns and crucibles for casting, closely resemble shapes found at Zhengzhou Erligang of the early Shang dynasty, other container shapes, such as pottery *li* and *gui* clearly differ from those of Erligang. Since "Yin followed the rites of Xia," it is understandable that there are remnants of the Xia cultural elements in the early Shang period, let alone the fact that there is a greater difference between the cultural elements of early and late Erlitou than between late Erlitou and early Shang. Excavated bronze vessels of the late Erlitou period also deserve special attention. They illustrate the degree of development reached in the art of bronze casting during the Xia dynasty and give credibility to the record stating that the Xia cast *ding*-like objects "from the tribute money of the nine provinces."

The early Shang culture, as represented by Erligang, was first discovered at the site of the same name in Zhengzhou, Henan, in 1952. At that time, the bronze industry had already reached a certain degree of development with bronze foundries and pottery workshops reflecting contemporaneous standards of production. Aside from *jue,* other bronze vessel shapes appeared, such as *li* and *jia.* These vessels mostly have constricted waists and flat bottoms, and the *jue* are outwardly different from those of Erlitou in that they do not have conspicuously concave waists, while their spouts are usually decorated on either side with a tiny upright. The legs of *li* vessels are hollow and awl-shaped. Animal mask motifs are relatively simple and usually flat except for the eyes, which are ball-shaped and in relief. Beside these main motifs, there are complementary rows of circles, a type of ornamental scheme often seen in early bronze decor. The *li, jue* and *jia* (Colorplate V and Figures 13 and 15), all with animal masks, are typical of this culture.

The golden age of the bronze culture took place during the late Shang period. Yinxu ("Wastes of Yin") at modern-day Anyang, Henan Province, was the site of the capital of the Shang kings from Pangeng[4] to Zhou[5] and was the post middle Shang political, economical and cultural center. It is the depository of a large number of precious cultural relics from late Shang. This is where bronze art developed to a climax, and it is from here that the culture and technology of the Shang extended widely beyond its area of political control. In fact, bronze articles of this period have been discovered in all other areas of the country marked by Shang culture. Many types are unprecedented, especially various categories of fine wine vessels, which reflect the life of wanton extravagance led by the slave-owning nobles of the Shang dynasty. Yet since such people used large amounts of grain to make wine, the vessels indirectly contributed to an increase in agricultural production. Compared with that of the Erligang period, the decoration of these bronzes has a more profound religious significance and, in most cases, makes use of exaggerated shapes to create a solemn atmosphere. The structural content of the design clearly distinguishes primary and secondary elements, and the engraving technique is a combination of high and low relief. Background motifs are frequently in low relief to set off a main design in high relief. Some of the vessels, or parts of them, are lively and skillful imitations of animal shapes. This is exemplified by the following late Shang objects from Anyang in the exhibition; the 畏 *ding* (Figure 17), the

天父乙 *gong* (Colorplate VIII) and the 几 *zun* (Figure 16), cooking vessels which display ingenious concepts and superb craftsmanship.

Among Shang dynasty handicrafts other than bronzes, jade and pottery also made great progress. Vestiges of bone workshops and pottery kilns have been discovered at both Yanshi and Zhengzhou in Henan. Besides the already existing gray and black pottery, there were stonewares, white potteries made of porcelaneous clay and proto-porcelains. They were fired at around 1000 to 1200° C., with a very low degree of porosity. Fine decorative patterns are carved on the surface of the white potteries, the stonewares are stamped with various ornamental schemes and the proto-porcelains covered with a yellowish-green glassy glaze. This glaze and its colorant are basically the same as those used in later celadons.

The production of jade, bone and stone articles was also delicate and refined. Besides being worn as pendants, they were made as ritual articles used in sacrifices and as tokens of political power. *Bi, yuan, huan, huang, jue, cong, gui, zhang, xi, guan* and *zhu*[6] were among the categories of objects carved in jade and bones. Techniques included deep and shallow carving, relief and openwork, as well as carving in the round, and such tools and abrasives as the drill and tallium were already in use for the making of jade articles. Jade carving in China can be traced back to the Neolithic period, and objects in this exhibition, including the *cong* (Colorplate I), the ceremonial blade (Figure 10) and the animal mask pendant (Figure 8), are products of the late phase of that period. To create such exquisite objects with the simple and crude tools of the time is hardly conceivable. The Shang jade axe (Figure 23) and the notched *xuanji* disc of agate (Figure 22), made as ritual objects, are plain, yet they display a perfection of carving that required a high level of craftsmanship and a certain amount of specialization. In the Shang dynasty, jade and semiprecious stones were also utilized in the inlaid decoration of bronze vessels. The bronze square *yue* axe in the exhibition (Colorplate VII) is inlaid with small pieces of turquoise forming cruciform motifs. This type of decorative technique can be seen among bronze objects excavated at the site of Erlitou, Yanshi, but a *yue* of this gigantic size is a rarity among such objects.

In the 11th century B.C., the Western Zhou dynasty replaced the Shang to rule China. Bronze manufacture during the early period followed in the steps of the Shang. However, because of the wide-scale creation of fiefs and feudal lords and because of the establishment of the patriarchal clan system, the early Zhou used blood ties in conjunction with the feudal system to preserve their political power. The production of bronze ritual and sacrificial objects increased accordingly. Moreover, it became popular to inscribe bronze vessels with records of such great events as the maker's appointment to an official position, conferment or victory in battle. Quite a few of these vessels are important historical documents today. The decoration of bronze vessels continued to use the animal mask motif of the Shang dynasty, but the bird motif, which was rarely seen before this time, became popular. Among the exhibits, the E Shu *gui* (Figure 27), the Kui Gu square *zun* (Figure 29), the Father Geng *zhi* (Figure 30) and the *you* with chevrons and square meanders (Colorplate IX) present imposing and sturdy shapes, with designs organized in a dignified and refined manner. In addition, all these vessels display extremely beautiful bird motifs. After the early Western Zhou period, other decorative motifs appeared such as the "pseudo meander", "double ring" and "dissolved *kui* dragon," The Shi Ju square *yi* (Colorplate XI) is a superior example of an association between "dissolved dragon *kui*" and "pseudo meander" motifs. The body and cover of this vessel are each inscribed with a 66-character text, which records in detail an exchange of gifts between Shi Ju and King Gong at a banquet given by the king and explains that Shi Ju made the vessel for his ancestors to mark this glorious occasion. In late Western Zhou, the earlier animal mask, the *kui* dragon and the bird motif gradually disappeared from the repertory of bronze designs or became subsidiary motifs of minor importance. Conversely, the meander, double ring, rows of scale and dissolved *kui* motifs became very popular. In general, the cloud thunder pattern was not used for background, and, as a result, the vessels give the feeling of being coarser.

In 770 B.C., the Zhou King Ping's move to the east marked the beginning of the Eastern Zhou. This was an important political turning point. Henceforth, there was an acceleration in the process of annexations among the feudal states, and the struggle for hegemony very naturally spurred further prosperity in the crafts and commerce. As a result, the cities in the various states were on the upsurge. There was also an increase in the number of bronzes made for the feudal princes and senior officials of the various states. These included ritual objects, such as *ding, dui, dou, bi* (ladles), *hu, jian, yi, pan* and *zhong;*[7] weapons such as swords, spears and arrowheads; horse and chariot fittings such as hubcaps and bridle bits; tools such as knives; and daily utensils such as mirrors and belt hooks. Outstanding achievements took place in the technique of sectional casting and soldering. Some of the more complicated vessels were first cast in sections and then soldered together, a process which created the proper conditions for the manufacture of a great diversity of shapes, and enabled a unit of a composite ornamental scheme to be stamped repeatedly on a vessel to achieve an overall motif of the same pattern. Such intricate decorative patterns as coiled dragons or coiled snakes could be meticulously rendered in one small unit. In addition, the wide use of iron implements at that time provided bronze makers with hard, sharp tools which enabled them to refine their techniques. Pure copper inlay and the use of sharp blades to incise hair-thin pictorial patterns on the surface of finished vessels were outstanding technical innovations. Such new technical practices were to play a major role in the development of the Warring States bronze industry in improving productivity, as well as the standardization and marketability of its products.

The *ding* with coiled dragon motif (Figure 42), the *hu* with feather motif (Figure 41), and *dui* with inlaid geometric designs (Figure 43) and the mirror with four tigers (Figure 44) are excellent examples of Warring States bronze art. They bring to extreme refinement the kind of minute and elaborate decoration which prevailed during the late Chunqiu period. This is also the time when the technique of inlaying bronze objects with gold, silver, copper and stones reached its peak.

The art of jade carving from the Western Zhou to the Warring States period should also be mentioned at this point. Various carved human and animal forms appeared during that period, some with delicate patterns, others in exquisite openwork. The handsome pendant with bird design (Figure 38) and openwork *huang* dragon-headed pendant with grain pattern (Figure 47) belong to this category of objects.

The manufacture of lacquer stands out among the burgeoning crafts of the Warring States, Qin and Han dynasties. At that time, the art of making lacquer was already well developed. Not only can lacquer be used to prevent the decay of objects, it can also absorb various pigments for the painting of designs. This device is more convenient and lively than carving and engraving, and, as a result, its utilization in objects of daily use expanded very rapidly. Large numbers of lacquer pieces of the Warring States period have been unearthed in burial sites at Xinyang, Henan; Jiangling, Hubei; Changsha, Hunan and Chengdu, Sichuan. In the Western Han period, the Shu and Guanghan Prefectures (in present-day eastern Jintang County, Sichuan Province) were famous for their lacquers. At the time, the division of labor in lacquer production was very detailed. The names of workers appearing on lacquer vessels include makers of plain lacquer, appliers, finishers, bronze handle gilders, painters, carvers, polishers and inspectors. In the middle of the Western Han, lacquer objects were commonly mounted in gilding, gold or silver and were known as "mounted vessels". Gilding, gold or silver was also used for the ears or handles of cups and ladles. This is why there were "bronze handle gilders" among the workers. The "silver mouth and yellow ears" and "gold inlaid cup of Shu" mentioned in the Han dynasty writer Huan Kuan's *Yantie Lun (Discourses on Salt and Iron)* describe just this type of vessel. The text goes on to say: "One cup employs the strength of a hundred men, one door screen the effort of ten thousand." This seems ample proof that lacquer was manufactured on a grand scale. The dish with cloud motifs in this exhibition (Colorplate XVII) is a product of the Western Han.

Along with lacquers and just as flourishing, ceramics came to be used as substitutes for bronzes. After the appearance of proto-porcelain in the Shang dynasty, the firing of ceramics gradually improved through the Warring States, Qin and Han periods, and, together with lacquers, ceramics were basically able to replace bronzes in satisfying people's daily needs. In fact, quite a few ceramic shapes of the early

period imitate bronze ones such as *zun, hu, xi, yi, lei* and *dou.* [8] The Eastern Han kiln site discovered at Shangyu, Zhejiang, yielded ceramic sherds fired at approximately 1310° plus or minus 20° C., with a water absorption rate of 0.28 %, and a ferric and titanic oxide content of 1.64 %, which meet the requirements for standard celadons.

The Three Kingdoms, Eastern and Western Jin and Northern and Southern dynasties correspond to a period of great upheaval in Chinese feudal society. A large number of refugees crossed the Yangzi and migrated south. The advanced technology and labor force of the Central Plain went with them, increasing the rate of social and economic growth in the region of the middle and lower Yangzi. One result is that celadons which had originally developed in the Jiangsu and Zhejiang region made further progress, and the appearance of the "dragon kiln" caused the firing of these wares to reach a new level of quality. Shangyu, Shaoxing, Xiaoshan, Yuyao and Lishui in Zhejiang Province became important production centers of celadons. Their development soon influenced kilns in Jiangsu, Jiangxi and Fujian. Celadon glazes of the time look grassy green with bluish-green highlights, and major shapes include bowls, jars, vases, basins, washbasins, tiger cubs and the granary-shaped jars inscribed with the character 廩 (*lin*) for "granary". Before the Eastern Jin, the decoration consisted essentially of net, pearl and water caltrop patterns, as well as applied rows of animal heads, birds, *bixie,* immortals and Buddhas. After the Eastern Jin, such ornamental schemes as rows of overlapping lotus petals appeared, and the decoration of the green-glazed surface with spots of dark brown became gradually popular. In this exhibition, the Western Jin is represented by a jar with architectural elements and human figurines (Colorplate XVI), a frog-shaped water container (Figure 56) and the Eastern Jin by a ram (Front Cover). The shapes, glazes and decoration of these very fine pieces are fully representative of the two Jin periods.

The Sui and Tang dynasties marked the first major period of unity in the Chinese feudal society since the Qin and Han dynasties. Social and economic conditions improved greatly, as did domestic relationships. Externally, China developed extensive contacts with many Asian nations, including present-day Korea, Japan, India, Pakistan, Afghanistan, Iran and Syria. The capital at Chang'an (present-day Xi'an, Shaanxi) became a domestic and international center for political, economic and cultural exchange. The art and culture of the Tang dynasty created an unprecedented atmosphere of prosperity. In the south, ceramics included the famous Yue celadons with warm, smooth, jade-like glazes and refined shapes. In the north, black and white glazed wares also developed greatly. For example, Henan abounded in kilns producing black-glazed wares like those in Gong County, the Huangdao kiln in Jia County and the Duandian kiln at Lushan, while Quyang in Hebei, Gong and Mi Counties in Henan and Dayi in Sichuan were famous for their white-glazed wares. In recent years, the site of the long-renowned Xing kiln has been discovered at Qi village, Lincheng, in Hebei. This is most reliable evidence in support of the pieces which we traditionally recognize as being Tang "Xingyao". The white-glazed porcelain bowl (Figure 73) in this exhibition has been identified as a product of the Xing kiln.

During the Tang dynasty, new achievements took place in the field of polychrome glazed wares. The Huangdao kiln of Jia County in Henan and the Tong-guan kiln at Changsha in Hunan were both famous for such glazes. The former favored blue colors applied in a slapdash, vivid, vigorous manner on a black-glazed ground; the latter preferred brownish-green spots applied more systematically on a yellowish-green glazed ground and, at times, went as far as using applied or painted elements with definite thematic contents.

The two-eared jarlet with color blotches on a black glaze (Figure 72) is a typical example of the excellent glaze of the Huangdao kiln in Jia County. Of course, where Tang polychrome glazes are concerned, the gorgeous three-color ware is even more popular. It was a type of lead-glazed ware. A large quantity of this ware had already been produced during the Han dynasty, but by Tang times it developed to the point where minerals, such as copper oxide, iron oxide and cobalt oxide were added to the transparent lead and quartz to serve as colorants for various glazes, which were painted onto the same vessel to produce such various colors as green, yellowish-green and blue. This was the Tang three-color ware, which due to its low firing temperature, porous body and high rate of water absorption, was rarely used for objects of daily use. The bulk of it consists of toys and sculptures used in burials (mingqi), and, of these, the figurines reflect with particular vividness the various aspects of society as it existed at the time. The two Tang three-color female figurines (Colorplate XXII and Figure 67) exhibit the most fashionable women's dress of the high Tang period. One of these women even wears a "wind hat", which was used on outings by northern women as a shield against wind and sand.

Most Tang horses were famous breeds from Persia and Arabia, and because the monarchs of the period were obsessed with these animals, the Tang dynasty did not lack in famous painters of horses. Perfectly proportioned and fully expressive as they are, these two haughty steeds and the white-glazed horse (Figure 71) demonstrate the degree of familiarity attained by artisans in representing horses. The three-color phoenix-headed ewer (Figure 70) and the three-legged tray with flying bird-and-cloud motifs (Figure 65) were influenced by Persian art and, from the point of view of shape and composition, are works that modify traditional Chinese styles.

During the Tang dynasty, an even more extraordinary manifestation of the complete assimilation of foreign art can be found in the achievements of Buddhist art. Since ancient times, monarchs had favored the propagation of religions as a means to pray for blessings and protection, and the Tang imperial house was no exception. After following Taoism, they also encouraged Buddhism with the erection of numerous temples, pagodas and cave temples. A great deal of Buddhist architecture and sculpture is still extant. Famous monks, such as Xuan Zang and Yijing, made special journeys to India and many other countries for the purpose of obtaining scriptures and "expanding the Law". The cave temples at present-day Yungang near Datong in Shanxi, Longmen near Luoyang in Henan, Dunhuang, Maijishan and Binglingsi in Gansu all belong to the body of northern Buddhist art that was erected first by the Northern Wei and flourished during the Sui and Tang dynasties. During this time, southern Buddhist architecture thrived and kept pace with that of the north. From the Tang dynasty writer Du Mu's poem, which says, "The 480 temples of the southern dynasty have innumerable high buildings in the misty rain," one can imagine how prosperous they were.

Buddhists worship icons, and many devotees of both sexes wishing to pay debts of gratitude for the education received from their parents and to obtain happiness in the next life vied with one another in commissioning effigies made as respectful offerings. In this exhibition, there is a group of bronze statuettes that range from the Northern Wei to the Tang and Song dynasties. Stylistically, the influence of Gandhāran art was quite pronounced during the Northern Wei period when drapery was detailed and clung to the body, but after the Sui and Tang dynasties, full cheeks, graceful postures and ample robes with flowing and lively folds fully embody the traditional qualities of Chinese art.

The Five Dynasties and the Northern and Southern Song dynasties arose from the establishment of separate regimes by Tang military governors during the late Tang dynasty. While the nation was united, dissension increased among the people. Qian Liu of the Five Dynasties period established a separate kingdom in the Hangzhou area. He built water conservation projects and let the people live in peace. The agriculture and economy of the Taihu area and the Zhejiang River basin developed accordingly.

During the more than seventy years of Wu-Yue rule, the Yue celadon kilns in Zhejiang carried forward the traditions of the Jin and Tang dynasties. This is illustrated by an object in this exhibition—a lively and ingenious Yueyao stoneware grain container with engraved decoration, handles on four sides, beautiful form and cover in the shape of a lotus leaf (Figure 74). It is a splendid example of Wu-Yue celadons of the Five Dynasties.

Chinese ceramics entered their prime in the Song dynasty when there were kilns practically all over the country. Where celadons are concerned, the north was famous for its Yaozhou kiln in Shaanxi and Linru kiln in Henan; in the south the Longquan kiln in Zhejiang and the Southern Song "official" kiln at Jiaotanxia in Hangzhou were outstanding. At this time, due to a better understanding of the ingredients capable of matching bodies and glazes and proper firing control, glaze colors could be changed from a grayish-brown

and a grayish-green to a bright, limpid, warm and smooth jade-like green. Among the objects selected for the exhibition, a Yaozhouyao celadon vase on three feet with carved decoration (Colorplate XXV) and a Longquan celadon *cong*-shaped vase (Colorplate XXVI) give a good idea of the quality reached in celadons in both the north and south during that period. The most famous white porcelains are those made at the Ding kiln at Quyang in Hubei, a kiln which was built in the Tang and flourished during the Five Dynasties and Northern Song. The bodies of Ding wares are generally very thin, and the color of their glazes tends toward a luminous and smooth ivory yellow. Their decoration consists of incised, carved and molded designs and is stylistically akin to that of Yaozhou, although the molded decoration seems to outshine that of the latter in intricacy and precision. Ding wares were generally fired upside down so that their rims are left unglazed and display a "hairy" edge. All the tribute wares were fitted with copper mouth rims, as in the outstanding plate with molded design of dragon and clouds (Figure 78) in this exhibition. Guan, Ge, Ru, Ding and Jun, often mentioned in ancient literature, were the five famous kilns of the Song period. The Ding and Jun kilns have been definitely located, but the sites of the kilns known traditionally as Guan, Ge and Ru are still open to question. Yanhedian in Nanxiang and Dayudian in Dongxiang, both in Linru, Henan Province, have yielded successfully fired celadon sherds. The color of these sherds tends to be a darker green than traditional Ru wares, and the transparent quality of their glaze is very unlike the muddy opacity of traditional pieces. Next is the Guan kiln of the Southern Song at Jiaotanxia, where many different varieties of ceramics have been unearthed. Among them are pieces with opaque glazes covered with a fine crackle, such as the porcellaneous Guan vase (Figure 83) in this exhibition. It is quite possible that this vase was produced at the Guan kiln of the Southern Song at Jiaotanxia. This vase, however, is quite different from the traditional Guan wares. Furthermore, traditional Ge wares and the crackled celadons excavated at Xikou, Longquan, are dissimilar in quality of body, glaze color and thickness. Contemporary scholars, who have made chemical and spectral analyses as well as microscopic structural studies of the body and glaze of imitation Ge pieces made at Jingdezhen during the Qing dynasty and of traditional Ge pieces, have concluded that traditional Ge ware may have been fired at Jingdezhen sometime after the Song. If this is the case, the location of the kiln even now remains a mystery.

Jun ware was primarily manufactured in Yu County in Henan, the best kilns being Juntai and Baguadong north of the city. In this exhibition, the very pale blue basin on three feet with drum nail decor (Figure 80) with its moonlight color must be an outstanding product of the Juntai kiln. Another example, a stoneware bowl with sky blue glaze and red suffusions (Colorplate XXIV), is primarily azure in color and has three splotches of red. These red and blue hues and opacity appear in many variations without any regularity. This is the result of reactions produced by dissimilar coloring agents in the copper and iron oxide contained in the glaze when in contact with phosphoric and silicic acids during firing in high temperature reducing conditions. Yu County, the principal producing area for Jun ware, is close to Jia County and famous Linru, which during the Tang dynasty produced polychrome glazes and celadons, respectively. It is therefore obvious that there was a definite relationship in the way firing methods were inherited, exploited and reacted on one another.

Song ceramics are also represented in this exhibition by a few products of the famous northern Cizhou kilns. They are noted for their shapes and decoration, which includes incising, engraving, carving, molding, painting and filling. These can be combined to offer many variations. Beside the kilns of Guantaizhen and Yezicun, Ci County in Hebei, kilns located at Pacun in Yu County, Dangyangyu in Xiuwu County, Hebiji in Tangyin County in Henan and Jiexiu in Shanxi also produced this kind of ware. The types of objects and their styles present local idiosyncracies, but it is also quite common to find typological and stylistic similarities between them due to the close proximity of the kilns. The most obvious characteristics of these Cizhou wares are the influence of contemporaneous painting and calligraphy and a markedly folk flavor.

Song painting followed the academic style of the Western Shu and Southern Tang, but in addition the literati's "ink play" style in monochrome painting was becoming popular. The literati were interested in the careful study of ink and brush techniques, which derive partially from folk painting. Conversely, it must be acknowledged that the "ink play" style of monochrome painting increased the popularity and raised the standards of folk painting. Therefore, the prevalence of this painting style in Cizhou wares since the Northern Song—besides being an element in ceramics—was intimately related to the achievement of simple brushwork in ink monochrome painting during the Song. Indeed, it may be that some paintings on Cizhou wares, with their pungency, frankness, fluidity and naturalness, cannot be matched by any literati painting, and it is no wonder that today's painters are so enthused by these ceramics that they regard their mode of expression as a model for their own calligraphy and painting. It also explains why this art, which was the creation of laboring people, has great vitality and smacks of the fragrant soil.

Since the Song and Yuan dynasties, Jingdezhen in Jiangxi has occupied a decisive position in the production of Chinese porcelains. During the Song dynasty, the Xianghu and Hutian kilns at Jingdezhen were famous for their *qingbai* porcelains, which in their purity and simplicity resemble Ding ware. Since the clay of Jingdezhen has a high iron content, the white in the glaze is not pure and after firing takes on a bluish tint. However, the glaze is as clear as glass and is commonly called "shadowy blue," a term reflecting the high esteem in which people hold this kind of porcelain.

The major distinguishing features of the Jingdezhen production are definitely the underglaze blue and the Ming and Qing polychrome porcelains. It is precisely due to the rather high iron content of Jingdezhen glazes and to the bluish tint which they emit after firing that underglaze blue patterns create a complementary effect.

Yuan was a period of improvement for Jingdezhen blue-and-white. Yuan glazes were generally thicker than those of the Ming and Qing. Once fired, the pieces displayed varying colors and lustres. The complex ornamental schemes are mostly based on motifs such as *ruyi*, palms, bamboos, chrysanthemums, sea waves and peony scrolls. The blue-and-white porcelain vase with peony scroll (Colorplate XXIX) and the foliated dish (Colorplate XXX) in this exhibition should be regarded as extremely successful works among the blue-and-white wares of the Yuan dynasty. The colorant for the blue in blue-and-white porcelain was cobalt. However, the source of cobalt differed with time, and the color of the blue varied accordingly. In the Ming dynasty, this variation became a distinctive stylistic feature in each period. The decor of the Xuande covered stem cup with floral scrolls (Figure 108) was painted with a type of cobalt known as "Suni-bo," and the color is a dark blue that penetrates into the body of the piece. The Chenghua dish with the Eight Buddhist Emblems (Colorplate XXXI) was painted wih *pingdeng* cobalt. The distinct and quietly elegant blue, together with the lustrous and smooth glaze, creates a feeling of elegance and softness. The Jiajing stem cup with figures in a landscape (Figure 112) was done in "Mohammedan" cobalt and has a rich color with a slightly shiny purplish-red tinge. All these chromatic features, which vary from one period to another, are due to the use of different ingredients.

Besides using cobalt for blue-and-white wares, underglaze painting at Jingdezhen also used copper for red decoration, but copper is an extremely unstable glaze ingredient because it can change considerably while in the kiln. As during the Yuan dynasty the use of pigments and temperature control were not adequate, and the copper red often turned reddish-brown. It was not until the Ming dynasty that copper red was produced successfully. By that time, monochrome copper reds were also produced, and the famous Yongle and Xuande bright red wares are incomparably beautiful. The glazes are all applied in two or three separate layers, and the metallic content of each layer differs. Copper resides in the lower layer, while such reducing agents as tin salts are added to the upper layer. When exposed to high-temperature firing, the copper element in the lower layer evaporates and penetrates the upper layer of the glazes, where it is affected by the reducing agent and turns red. Therefore, the red glazes of the Xuande period present irregular red dots and streaks which are scattered throughout the glaze layers and are not on one single plane. This technique produces a color much more beautiful than mixing copper directly with a one-layer glaze, but is very difficult to achieve because the copper changes easily with temperature fluctuations during firing and

the color remains unstable. For this reason the Xuande underglaze red porcelain dish in this exhibition (Figure 110) is an extremely rare masterpiece.

In addition to monochromes and underglaze painting, at the beginning of the middle Ming, Jingdezhen porcelain makers developed *doucai* ("contrasted colors"), *tiancai* ("filled-in colors") and *wucai* ("five colors") techniques. These types of polychrome techniques reached a climax during the Kangxi and Qianlong periods of the Qing dynasty. At that time, there was not only single-lined, flat painting in hard, transparent, high-fired colors usually known as *gucai* ("ancient colors"), but also an opaque white enamel which, just like the white powder used in painting, increased the varieties of color schemes. Such low-fired soft colors are usually known as *fencai* ("*famille rose* enamels"). In this exhibition, the Kangxi five-color porcelain vase with decoration inspired by an episode in the *Romance of the Three Kingdoms* (Colorplate XLIV) and the Yongzheng porcelain dish decorated with birds and flowers in overglaze enamels (Figure 145) suffice to represent the achievements attained in painted porcelains during this period.

Another major section of this exhibition, which is devoted to painting—from a scroll by the Ming master Shen Zhou through contemporary works—includes some of the greatest Ming and Qing paintings and calligraphies in the collection of the Shanghai Museum. Of course, Shen Zhou's work is separated by more than 1,700 years from the Warring States silk painting "Figure in a Dragon Boat," which was discovered a long time ago, and by more than 1,500 years from the silk painting recently found in the Western Han tomb of the Marquise of Dai at Mawangdui. The period from the Western Han to the Ming saw the splendid achievements of the Wei, Jin and Six Dynasties figure painters Gu Kaizhi, Lu Tanwei, Zhang Sengyou and Cao Zhongda. It also saw an unprecedented abundance of bird-and-flower, animal and landscape painting during the Sui and Tang dynasties, witnessed the refined skill of the Five Dynasties and Northern and Southern Song academics and the "ink play" of the literati, which brought about great developments in ink painting and brush and ink aesthetics in the Yuan dynasty. In the nine hundred some years from the Wei and Jin to the end of the Yuan, Chinese painting made a great contribution to world culture by carrying forward ancient and fine traditions. Within China, its achievements influenced all the other branches of arts and crafts. Sculpture, ceramics, lacquer and textiles were all deeply marked with characteristics found in contemporaneous painting.

In the middle Ming, the influence of the Southern Song academy was still very strong, as can be seen in this exhibition by Wu Wei's "Short Rest in the Shade of a Pine" (Figure 94), Lü Ji's "Teals Bathing" (Figure 96) and Lin Liang's "Jackdaws on a Withered Tree" (Figure 95). Whether they be landscape, figures, bird-and-flower or trees and rocks, all preserve the stylistic range and the special vigor of brush and ink of the Southern Song academy. Seen from another angle, it was the booming economy which prevailed at the time in the handicraft industry and commerce that produced numerous industrial and commercial cities. These cities brought about a concentration of painters which resulted in competing regional painting styles and schools. Throughout the Qing dynasty, painting styles grew out of regional schools. This is one of the major characteristics of the development of Ming and Qing painting.

First was the Zhe school, which developed in the region of Hangzhou in Zhejiang and carried forward the Southern Song academic style led by Dai Jin and Wu Wei. A large group of artists who adapted academic forms to new personal expressions emerged after them. For example, Xu Wei's "Fifth Month Lotus" (Figure 103) and Chen Hongshou's "Ruan Xiu Buying Wine" (Figure 104) are works by masters who developed their own schools within the Zhe school.

In the Suzhou area, the best-known Wu school artists were Shen Zhou, Wen Zhengming, Tang Yin and Qiu Ying. This school emphasized the Song and Yuan literati painting style, but also adopted the strong points of academic painting. Tang Yin and Qiu Ying, in particular, created meticulous and refined works that are especially appealing. All four of them are represented in this exhibition. Chen Chun ("Pomegranate and Mallow," Figure 102) and Lu Zhi ("Cloudy Peaks and a Valley Grove," Colorplate XXXIV) were both students of Wen Zhengming, as well as outstanding exponents of this school.

The Songjiang school was active in the Husong area during the late Ming and early Qing. Dong Qichang, who painted the "Landscape in the Style of Dong Beiyuan" (Colorplate XXXV), was a significant figure in this movement. The special characteristic of the Songjiang school was its emphasis on tradition and research in brush and ink techniques. During the early Qing, this school was extremely influential in the painting styles of the Shanghai, Songjiang, Changshu and Taicang regions. Wang Hui's "Wild Groves and Rushing Waterfall" (Figure 124) and Wang Yuanqi's "Landscape in the Manner of Ni Zan and Huang Gongwang" (Figure 125) amply demonstrate that, under this stylistic umbrella, the pursuit of antiquity had become a field where painters could not go any further. In his early years, the Changzhou painter Yun Shouping, contemporary and close friend of Wang Hui, also painstakingly copied the ancient masters. However, his flower painting mostly derives from direct observation of nature, and his achievements in capturing the spirit of flowers and plants are foremost among the flower painters of his generation. In fact, he was a major naturalistic flower painter of the Qing dynasty. Very few of his large-scale flower paintings remain, but there are many forgeries. "Chrysanthemums and Rocks" (Colorplate XLI) is one of his surviving masterpieces. He, along with the Four Wangs of the Early Qing (Wang Shimin, Wang Jian, Wang Hui and Wang Yuanqi) and the Catholic painter Wu Li, who painted the "Blue-and-Green Landscape in Imitation of Zhao Mengfu" (Colorplate XL) in this exhibition, were collectively called the Six Great Masters of the Early Qing.

During the early Qing, in addition to the Songjiang, Taicang and Yushan schools, there was a group of descendants and former officials of the late Ming imperial household who called themselves "leftovers" and either embraced Buddhism or Taoism or lost themselves in the wilderness. This group included famous people such as Shitao and Hongren of the Huangshan school in Anhui, Kuncan and Gong Xian of the Jinling school in Nanjing and Zhu Da and Luo Mu of the Jiangxi school. They advocated learning from nature and taking advantage of natural circumstances to express one's own feelings. They expected a work of art to have individuality, a style of its own and to avoid sinking into the rut of tradition. Included in this exhibition are Kuncan's bold and vigorous "Landscape" (Figure 129), Hongren's clear, fine, delicate "Pine and Rocks in the Yellow Sea" (Figure 128), Zhu Da's powerful and clever "Wild Geese Among Rushes" (Figure 130) and Shitao's robust and unconstrained "Wandering Around Mt. Huayang" (Colorplate XLII). Each has its own personality and is different from any of the others. Yet the artists had compatible views on the theory of painting; they were all of one mind.

By the middle of the Qing dynasty, many painters were gathered in Yangzhou, Jiangsu. The most famous among them were the Eight Yangzhou Eccentrics (Jin Nong, Huang Shen, Li Shan, Zheng Xie, Li Fangying, Wang Shishen, Gao Xiang and Luo Ping). There were also Hua Yan, Chen Xuan and Bian Shoumin. In the exhibition, Jin Nong's "Plum Blossoms" (Figure 136), Zheng Xie's "Bamboo and Rocks" (Figure 138), Li Shan's "Ink Lotus" (Figure 137), Luo Ping's "Zhong Kui" (Figure 139) and Hua Yan's "*Osmanthus Fragrans and Tree Pie*" (Figure 135) carry on the artistic viewpoints and technical achievements of masters such as Shitao and Zhu Da. By stressing personal impressions in their paintings of figures and birds and flowers, they opened up a new field full of poetry and joie de vivre. This painting school has had a deep and far-reaching influence on later modern Chinese painters.

Let us now turn for a moment to the development of Ming portraiture and Qing academic painting. During the Ming dynasty, besides the Zhe school and a handful of Wu school artists, most literati hardly got involved in portrait painting, which, however, was quite popular and highly successful at the court and among high officials. The Fujian painter Zeng Jing, who resided in Nanjing during the late Ming, was a master of realistic portraiture. His works were quiet and refined. For each portrait, he often applied dozens of layers of dry washes until he achieved a true-to-life image. In his "Portrait of Zhao Shi'e" (Colorplate XXXIII) in this exhibition, the figure is so lifelike that it seems to be ready to step out of the painting. Due to the patronage of the Qing monarchs, academic painting was also on the rise. Yuan Jiang's "Immortals' Palace in the Spring Mountains" (Figure 133) represents the artistic standards of Qing "ruled line" painting, and Shen Quan's "Pine and Cranes" (Colorplate

XLIII) is a combination of academic and foreign techniques. This manner of painting had a great influence on the decorative arts of the Qianlong and Jiaqing periods. Of course, this was also due to the patronage of the monarchs. The famous Guyuexuan enamels used on court porcelains are the best case in point.

In modern times, the Haipai, which was influenced by the Yangzhou school, arose at the right moment in Shanghai, the most advanced developing industrial and commercial city on the coast. Like the Yangzhou school, it was formed by painters congregating from various places. Xugu, Zhu Cheng, Zhao Zhiqian, Pu Hua, Ren Yi, Lu Hui, Ni Tian, Wu Jiaxian and Wu Changshuo were among the most famous of these painters. Stylistically, they all rejected old and decaying traditions and stood out for their freshness and vitality. In his "Loquats" (Figure 140), Xugu used the brush like a cutting knife with light ink in free sweeping strokes to depict branches and leaves. A few of the leaf blades are rendered with the tip of the brush in "scorched" ink and stand out from the light washes. It makes the orange loquats look good enough to eat. Ren Yi's "Fisherman" (Figure 141) reveals the artist's technical skill. It is as if "likeness was already present with just one or two strokes." In his "Peaches" (Figure 156), Wu Changshuo's use of brush and ink is entirely derived from his experience and skill in the calligraphy of inscriptions on ancient bronzes and stone tablets. The painting is "loose enough for a horse to run through and too tight for the wind to penetrate." This interaction of looseness and tightness creates a great momentum that permeates the whole painting. Many later painters took after Wu Changshuo, but most could only vaguely capture his outward forms and not his inner strength. However, Qi Baishi's "Quiet Delight of the Lotus Pond" (Colorplate LII) absorbs the strong points of the great master and transforms them into something very personal. Among the later painters who opened new paths while following Wu's approach, one can single out the late Pan Tianshou, whose attitude toward his art was similar to the way he behaved. It was mellow and serious. Regardless of layout or structure or whether he was using ink or color, each of his dots, each of his strokes was done with utmost care. As a result, the contents of any of his works can be reduced to one foot without looking cramped or enlarged to any dimension without looking sparse. In his "Bald Vulture" (Figure 160), the brush is strong and the ink dripping wet. Few painters in his generation matched his efficacy and training, and yet he was extremely modest and full of praise for the landscapes of his contemporary Huang Binhong, insisting that his own landscapes could not compare with them. This exhibition also includes a landscape by Huang Binhong (Figure 158), done when he was 83 years old. The brushwork resembles "bent iron and twisted steel." It is the result of a cultivation of Kun Can's and Cheng Sui's brush and ink methods and of his life-long "eager quest for the wondrous peaks" of famous mountains and great rivers. Among the modern paintings, there is also Xu Beihong's "Old Cypress" (Figure 159), which is bushy and dense. The brushwork is spontaneous, yet appropriately expresses the texture and light contrasts of the branches and trunk of the old cypress. It is a work that blends the best of Eastern and Western approaches. When all is said, Xu Beihong may well be regarded as a major contributor to the technical changes that took place in modern Chinese painting.

For the past hundred years, Chinese applied and decorative arts and crafts, such as ceramics, lacquer, ivory carving, cloisonné and other folk arts, have suffered from languishing and bleak conditions, and many techniques were lost with the death of craftsmen. However, after the establishment of New China, the nation placed great emphasis on applied arts with national characteristics and on folk art. It vigorously supported their revival and production and organized various specialized research institutions to elevate the level of creativity in this domain. As a result, many arts and crafts that had reached an impasse were reawakened and crafts already lost revived. The jadeite double vase with carved dragons (Colorplate XLIX) and the white jade vase with carved birds and chains (Figure 162) are objects carved since Liberation. When compared with the masterpieces of the Qianlong and Jiaqing eras, they show a degree of delicacy and care which is in no way inferior.

The foregoing description of this exhibition of treasures from the Shanghai Museum is a very sketchy summary of the development of 6,000 years of Chinese art. It is certainly not comprehensive, but in ancient China people used to say, "Taste one slice of meat from the cauldron to know the flavor within." Therefore, when viewing the exhibition it is not hard to imagine the long history and magnificent culture of the nation that produced these fine works of art. Nor is it hard to realize that the high level of achievement reached by this great ancient and highly civilized nation is the result of the wisdom and diligence which people of all ethnic groups have collectively exercised over the centuries.

Zheng Wei
Vice Director
Exhibition Research Department
Shanghai Museum

(1) *Dao* 刀 and *zuo* 凿.
(2) *Ling* 铃.
(3) 爵.
(4) Traditional dates for the reign of Pangeng: 1401–1374 B.C.
(5) Traditional dates for the reign of Zhou: 1154–1123 B.C.
(6) *Bi* 璧: a flat disc.
   *Yuan* 瑗: a ring or circlet.
   *Huan* 环: a ring or circlet.
   *Huang* 璜: a semi-circular ornament.
   *Jue* 玦: an incomplete ring with one segment cut out.
   *Cong* 琮: a tube; in cross-section a circle within a square (see Colorplate I).
   *Gui* 圭: a tablet.
   *Zhang* 璋: a sceptre.
   *Xi* 觽: a bodkin.
   *Guan* 管: a tube or pipe.
   *Zhu* 珠: a bead.
(7) *Ding* 鼎: a tripod cauldron with solid legs (see Colorplate X).
   *Dui* 敦: a spherical tripod that opens to become two hemispherical bowls (see Figure 43).
   *Dou* 豆: a spherical stem cup that opens to become two hemispherical stem cups.
   *Bi* 匕: ladle.
   *Hu* 壶: a vase-shaped vessel with narrowed neck and swelling body (see Figure 40).
   *Jian* 鉴: a large basin.
   *Yi* 匜: a shallow legged pouring vessel with handle and elongated spout (see Colorplate XIII).
   *Pan* 盘: a large flat basin.
   *Zhong* 钟: a clapperless bell (see Figure 35).
(8) *Zun* 尊: a vase-shaped vessel with trumpet mouth and square shoulders (see Figure 29).
   *Hu* 壶. See footnote (7) above.
   *Xi* 洗: a washbasin.
   *Yi* 匜. See footnote (7) above.
   *Lei* 罍: a vase-shaped vessel with constricted neck, swelling mid-section and narrow foot (see Figure 31).
   *Dou* 豆. See footnote (7) above.

■ BEIJING

▲ Liyu, Hunyuan

● Quyang

● Lincheng

▲ Shilou
● Jiexiu
● Yidu
○ Longshan
▲ Anyang
○ Dawenkou

▲ Changzhi
● Tangyin

○ Majiayao
● Tongchuan

Houma △
Erlitou, Yanshi
Yangshaocun
Qinyang
○ Miaodigou ○ ○ Gongxian
▲ Zhengzhou
○ Shilingxia
△ ▲ ● Mixian
▲ Baoji ▲ Fufeng
Jincun ▲▲ ● Dengfeng
Luoyang ● Yuxian
● Linru
● Huangdao, Jiaxian
Lushan

■ Yangzhou
Xiangshan ○
○ ■ Nanjing ● Changzhou
Jiangning ● Taicang
● Suzhou ■ SHANGHAI
▲ Suixian
● Songjiang
Liangzhu
Lin'an ○ ○ Hangzhou
● Dayi ● Huangshan ○ Hemudu
■ Xiaoshan ○ Shangyu
Shaoxing

○ Jingdezhen ●
● Lishui

○ Longquan
● Changsha

● Dehua

Legend:
Main bronze sites
objects ▲
foundries △

Main ceramic sites
objects ○
kilns ●

Main painting schools ■

## DETAIL MAP OF SHANGHAI MUNICIPALITY

Jiangsu Province

Yangzi River

Jiadingxian

Baoshanxian

Chuanshaxian

Siqiancun

Fuquanshan
•Guoyuancun

Qingpuxian
•Songze

Shanghaixian

•Guangfulin

•Tangmiaocun

Maqiao

Nanhuixian

Songjiangxian

Fengxian

Tinglin

Jinshanxian

Zhelin

Chashan

Qijiadun•

Zhejiang Province

Legend: ///// Bamboo Ridge

I

II

III

IV

VI

V

VII

VIII

IX

XI

XII

XIII

XIV

XVI

XVII

XVIII

XIX

XX

XXI

XXII

XXV

XXVI

XXIX

牡丹庭院又春深一寸
光陰萬兩金拂曙起來
人解只緣難放惜花心
唐寅

誰將尺素寫余真想像差堪擬逸民雨目章絁
存故我猶看寧有儔特人落心本自甘怡漢慵
牲偏宜神隱論一秔自賁圖形何必是
麒麟
親余者多矣缺雜其似先嶝畫謂逼真
遂頌謨藏之將年六十有四天礫甲子仲
冬日塞鄉識

胡王之儼其而媛氣系六守即之也
溫而鐵閯不可干嘉門無雾覽余
地之餘有為有守呈碩人之寛權
也三十年蒿昭迎身敷言敷之內謔
則三十年後感愴形似恒侶之問鳴
呼塞芳塞于吾師噫啫薰芳薰芳
微吾師高難師

庚辰仰秋門人馬櫨荀薰沐頓首薰并書

天啓甲子冬日審觀寫

屏間雲綵空中落天外雲峰闥處明
時聽朗吟林答應蒼崖懸有卧遊人
嘉靖壬子仲春㝹山陸治製

XXXIV

黄子久有層巒疊嶂

翠圖隆隆精妙而景太

繁此朱能取弱如金

謂尚堂動之不苦小

苑雄壯耳

壬戌秋八月

之牟

XXXVI

XXXVII

XXXVIII

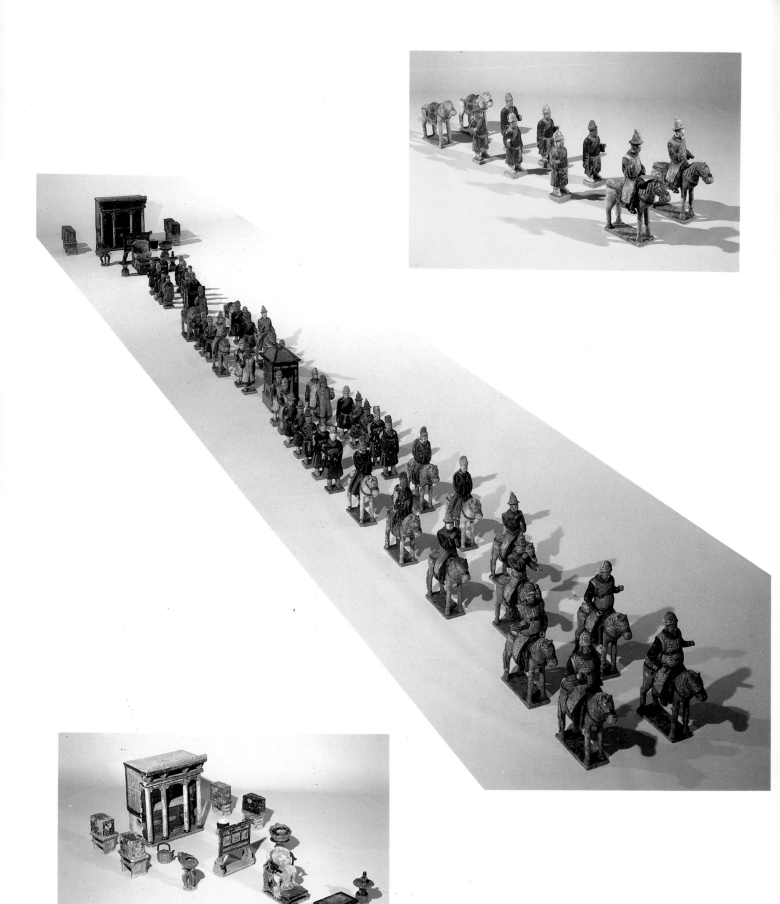

一峰邪盡一峰環折經崎
嶇遠碧端恁尺詣天開對
抄濚迴萬壑起眉端花
梁石引煙凭庋冒膽無
從鳥遺看擬欲尋源最
深處流露繰繰隱仙壇
遊華陽山中作枯此
清湘石濤濟

XLII

XLIII

XLV

XLVI

XLVII

XLIX

L

LI

FRONT COVER: **Ram** (Eastern Jin period, 317–419 A.D.), Celadon Stoneware, no. 57

BACK COVER: **"Tao Yuanming Admiring Chrysanthemums" by Zheng Fujia** (Qing dynasty, Qianlong period, 1736–1795 A.D.), Bamboo Carving, no. 151

## COLORPLATE IDENTIFICATION

# CHRONOLOGY

**NEOLITHIC** (as applied to the Shanghai region)
    Hemudu ..........................................ca.5,000 B.C.
    Majiabang .......................................ca. 5100–3900 B.C.
    Songze ..........................................ca. 3800–2700 B.C.
    Liangzhu ........................................ca. 2700–1900 B.C.

**XIA** .................................................21st–16th century B.C.

**SHANG** .............................................16th–11th century B.C.
    Erligang period .......................16th–14th century B.C.
    Early Anyang period ..................14th century B.C.
    Middle Anyang period ...............13th–12th century B.C.
    Late Anyang period ..................12th–11th century B.C.

**WESTERN ZHOU** ..................................Late 11th century–770 B.C.

**EASTERN ZHOU** ...................................770–256 B.C.
    Chunqiu (Spring and Autumn Annals Period) ........770–476 B.C.
    Warring States ...............................476–221 B.C.

**QIN** ................................................221–206 B.C.

**WESTERN HAN** ...................................206 B.C.–24 A.D.

**EASTERN HAN** ....................................25– 220

**THREE KINGDOMS** ...............................220– 265

**WESTERN JIN** .....................................226– 316

**EASTERN JIN** ......................................317– 420

**SIX DYNASTIES** ...................................420– 589
    Northern Wei ....................................386–534

**SUI** ................................................581– 618

**TANG** ..............................................618– 907

**FIVE DYNASTIES** .................................907– 960

**LIAO** ..............................................916–1125

**SONG** .............................................960–1279
    Northern Song ..................................960–1126
    Southern Song ..................................1127–1279

**JIN** ................................................1115–1234

**YUAN** (Mongols) .................................1271–1368

**MING** .............................................1368–1644

| | | | |
|---|---|---|---|
| Hongwu | 1368–1398 | Hongzhi | 1488–1505 |
| Jianwen | 1399–1402 | Zhengde | 1506–1521 |
| Yongle | 1403–1424 | Jiajing | 1522–1566 |
| Xuande | 1426–1435 | Longqing | 1567–1572 |
| Zhengtong | 1436–1449 | Wanli | 1573–1620 |
| Jingtai | 1450–1456 | Taichang | 1620 |
| Tianshun | 1457–1464 | Tianqi | 1621–1627 |
| Chenghua | 1465–1487 | Chongzhen | 1628–1644 |

**QING** .............................................1644–1911

| | | | |
|---|---|---|---|
| Shunzhi | 1644–1661 | Daoguang | 1821–1850 |
| Kangxi | 1662–1722 | Xianfeng | 1851–1861 |
| Yongzheng | 1723–1735 | Tongzhi | 1862–1874 |
| Qianlong | 1736–1795 | Guangxu | 1875–1908 |
| Jiaqing | 1796–1820 | Xuantong | 1909–1911 |

**CONTEMPORARY** .................................1911–

1. *Dou* (Neolithic age, Songze culture, 4,950–5,860 years ago), Grey Pottery.

2. Pig-shaped *Yi* (Neolithic age, Songze culture, 4,950–5,860 years ago), Grey Pottery.

3. *Ding* (Neolithic age, Songze culture, 4,950–5,860 years ago), Clay Mixed with Fine Sand.

4. Openwork *Hu* Jar (Neolithic age, Songze culture, 4,950–5,860 years ago), Black Pottery.

6. *He* with Lid (Neolithic age, Liangzhu culture, 3,920–4,710 years ago), Black Pottery.

71

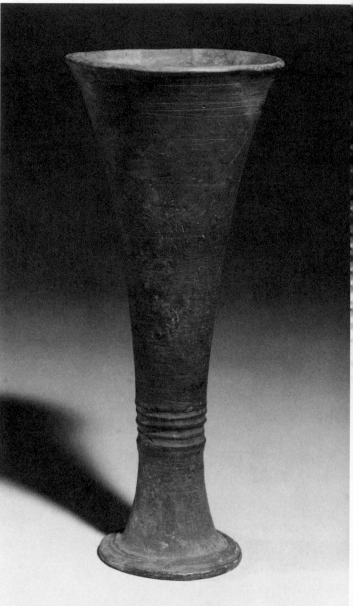

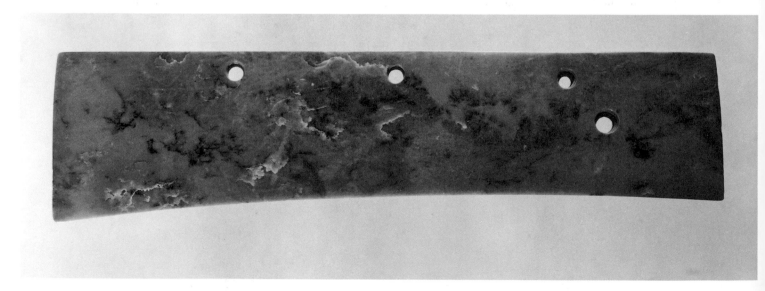

8. Animal Mask Pendant (Neolithic age, Liangzhu culture, about 3,920–4,710 years ago), Jade.

12. *Gu* (Shang dynasty, 16th–11th century B.C.), Black Pottery.

10. Ceremonial Blade (Neolithic age), Jade.

15. *Jia* with Animal Mask (Shang dynasty, Erligang phase, 16th – 14th century B.C.), Bronze.

13. *Li* with Animal Masks (Shang dynasty, Erligang phase, 16th–14th century B.C.), Bronze.

17. *Ding,* Inscribed (Shang dynasty, late Anyang phase, 12th–11th century B.C.), Bronze.

16. *Zun,* Inscribed (Shang dynasty, middle Anyang phase, 13th–12th century B.C.), Bronze.

18. *Gui,* Inscribed *You Fu Kui* (Shang dynasty, late Anyang phase, 12th–11th century B.C.), Bronze.

21. *You*-shaped Vessel, Inscribed (Shang dynasty, late Anyang phase, 12th–11th century B.C.), Bronze.

23. Ceremonial Axe (Late Shang dynasty, 14th–11th century B.C.), Jade.

22. Notched *Xuanji* Disc (Shang dynasty, 16th–11th century B.C.), Agate.

26. *Square Ding,* Inscribed *Huo Fu Kui* (Early Western
    Zhou period, 11th–10th century B.C.), Bronze.
27. *Gui,* Inscribed *E Shu* (Early Western Zhou period,
    11th–10th century B.C.), Bronze.

29. Square *Zun*, Inscribed *Kui Gu* (Early Western Zhou period, 11th–10th century B.C.), Bronze.

30. *Zhi*, Inscribed *Fu Geng* (Early Western Zhou period, 11th–10th century B.C.), Bronze.

31. Square *Lei*, Inscribed *Fu Ding* (Early Western Zhou period, 11th–10th century B.C.), Bronze.

34.  *Ling*, Inscribed *Fu Zhong Yi* (Late Western Zhou period, 9th century –771 B.C.), Bronze.

35.  Large *Zhong* Bell with Dragon Decor (Late Western Zhou period, 9th century – 771 B.C.), Bronze.

*Bo* Bell with Four Tigers (Late Western Zhou period, 9th century –771 B.C.), Bronze.

Pendant with Bird Design (Western Zhou period, 11th century –771 B.C.), Jade.

*Gui* (Western Zhou period, ca. 11th century –771 B.C.), Grey Pottery.

40. *Hu* with Birds, Animals and Dragons (Late Chunqiu period, second half of the 6th century –476 B.C.), Bronze.

41. *Hu* (Late Chunqiu period, second half of 6th century –476 B.C.), Bronze.

42. *Ding* with Coiled Dragon Motif (Warring States Period, 475–2 B.C.), Bronze.

43. *Dui* Inlaid with Geometric Designs (Warring States Period, 47 221 B.C.), Bronze.

44. Mirror with Four Tigers (Warring States period, 475–221 B.C. Bronze.

46. *Ding* with a Dragon's Head (Warring States period, 475–221 B.C.), Celadon Glazed Stoneware.

47. *Huang* Dragon-headed Pendant with Grain Pattern (Warring States period, 475–221 B.C.), Jade.

45. Jarlet with Handle and Nipple Feet (Warring States period, 475–221 B.C.), Impressed Pottery.

49. *Bi* Disc with *Kui* Dragons and Animal Masks,
    (Han dynasty, 206 B.C. –220 A.D.), Jade.

52. Mirror with Various Supernatural Beings
    (Eastern Han period, dated 187 A.D.), Bronze.

53. Dog (Han dynasty, 206 B.C.–220 A.D.), Brown-glazed Pottery.
56. Frog-shaped Water Container (Western Jin period, 265–316 A.D.),
    Celadon Stoneware.

59.  Standing Buddha (Northern Wei period, 386–534 A.D.), Bronze.
58.  Bodhisattva Padmapani (Northern Wei period 501 A.D.), Gilt Bronze.

62. Guanyin (Tang dynasty, 618–907 A.D.), Gilt Bronze.
61. Seated Buddha (Tang dynasty, 618–907 A.D.), Gilt Bronze.

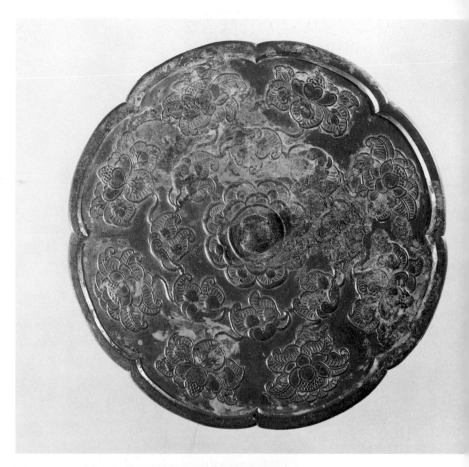

64. Mallow-shaped Mirror (Tang dynasty, 618–907 A.D.), Bronze.

65. Tray with Three Feet and Decoration of Flying Birds and Cloud Scrolls (Tang dynasty, 618–907 A.D.), Polychrome Glazed Pottery.

68. Seated Female Figurine (Tang dynasty, 618–907 A.D.), Polychrome Glazed Pottery.

67. Female Rider in Foreign Attire (Tang dynasty, 618–907 A.D.), Polychrome Glazed Pottery.

69. Female Figurine (Tang dynasty, 618–907 A.D.), Painted and Gilded Pottery.

70. Phoenix-headed Pitcher (Tang dynasty, 618–907 A.D.), Polychrome Glazed
Pottery.

72. Two-eared Jarlet (Tang dynasty, 618–907 A.D.), Stoneware with Color
Blotches on a Black Glaze.

71.  Horse (Tang dynasty, 618–907 A.D.), Pottery with Underglaze White Spots.

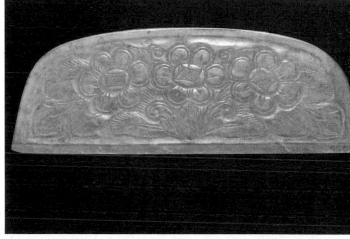

74. Grain Container with Four Handles and Engraved Decoration (Five Dynasties period, 907–960 A.D.), *Yue* Ware.

75. Comb Top with Floral Motif (Northern Song dynasty, 960–1127 A.D.), Jade.

73. Bowl (Tang dynasty, 618–907 A.D.), Xing Ware Porcelain.

77. Mahāsthāmaprāpta (Song dynasty,
960–1279 A.D.), Gilt Bronze.

78. Porcelain Plate with Molded Design of Dragon and Clouds (Northern Song dynasty, 960–1127 A.D.), Ding Ware.

80. Stoneware Basin on Three Feet with Drum Nail Decor (Northern Song dynasty, 960–1127 A.D.), Jun Ware.

83. Vase (Southern Song dynasty, 1127–1279 A.D.), Porcellaneous Guan Ware.

82. Porcellaneous Vase with Pierced Ears (Southern Song dynasty, 1127–1279 A.D.), Ge Ware.

90. Stem Cup with Shufu Glaze and Impressed Decoration of Dragons in Clouds (Yuan dynast, 1271–1368 A.D.) Jingde, Porcelain.

85. Bowl (Southern Song dynasty, 1127–1279 A.D.), Lacquer.

88. Stoneware Pillow in the Shape of a Reclining Baby, Decorated with a Poem (Jin dynasty, 11 1234 A.D.), Pacun Ware.

93. Foliated Platter Decorated in Underglaze Red with a Spray of Peonies (Late Yuan to early Ming, 14th century A.D.), Jingde, Porcelain.

94. "Short Rest in the Shade of a Pine" by Wu Wei (Ming dynasty, 1368–1644 A.D.), Hanging Scroll on Silk.

95. "Jackdaws on a Withered Tree" by Lin
    Liang (Ming dynasty, 1368–1644 A.D.),
    Hanging Scroll on Paper.

96. "Teals Bathing" by Lü Ji (Ming dynasty, 1368–1644 A.D.), Hanging Scroll on Silk.

弘治甲寅秋八月沈周臨
大癡道人筆意

97. "Landscape in the Style of Da Chi" by Shen Zhou (Ming dynasty, dated 1494 A.D.),
Hanging Scroll on Paper.

98. "Sitting Cross-legged in a Thatched Hut" by Wen Zhengming
(Ming dynasty, 1368–1644 A.D.), Hanging Scroll on Paper.

100. "Sitting Cross-legged at the Foot of a Mountain" by Qiu Ying (Ming dynasty, 1368–1644 A.D.), Hanging Scroll on Paper.

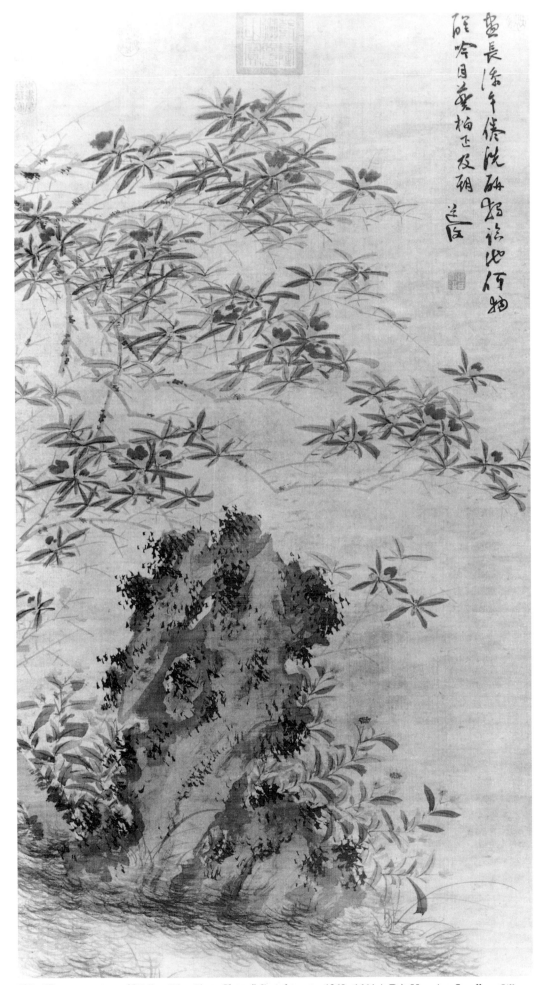

102. "Pomegranate and Mallow" by Chen Chun (Ming dynasty, 1368–1644 A.D.), Hanging Scroll on Silk.

103. "Fifth Month Lotus" by Xu Wei (Ming dynasty, 1368–1644 A.D.),
Hanging Scroll on Paper.

104. "Ruan Xiu Buying Wine" by Chen Hongshou (Ming dynasty, 1368–1644 A.D.), Hanging Scroll on Silk.

112. Blue-and-white Porcelain Stem Cup Decorated with Figures in a Landscape (Ming dynasty, Jiajing reign, 1522–1566 A.D.), Jingde Ware.

107. Two-eared Covered Jar, White Porcelain with Incised Floral Sprays, (Ming dynasty, Yongle reign, 1403–1424 A.D.), Jingde Ware.

108. Blue-and-white Covered Cup with Floral Design (Ming dynasty, Xuande reign, 1426–1435 A.D.), Jingde Ware.

109. Blue-and-white Porcelain Dish with Peony (Ming dynasty, Xuande reig
1426–1435 A.D.), Jingde Ware.

115. Procession of Honor Guard Figurines (Ming dynasty, 1368–1644 A.D.),
Polychrome Pottery. General view and details.

117. Water Spurting Basin (Ming dynasty, 1368–1644 A.D.), Bronze.

116. Three-legged Incense Burner with Floral Pattern (Ming dynasty, 1368–1644 A.D.), cloisonné.

119a. Aromatics Container Carved by Zhu Xiaosong (Ming dynasty, 1368–1644 A.D.), Bamboo.

119b. Rubbing of Design.

118. Box with Peony Decoration (Ming dynasty, Xuande period, 1426–1435 A.D.), Carved Red Lacquer.

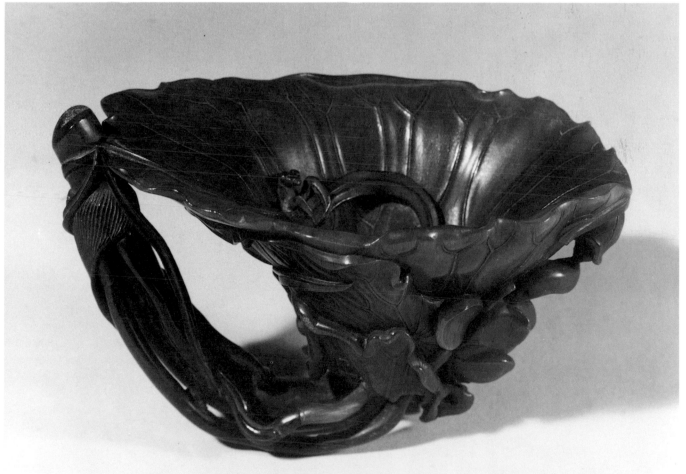

120. Raft Cup carved by Bao Tiancheng (Ming dynasty, 1368–1644 A.D.), Rhinoceros Horn.
121. Cup carved by Youkan (Ming dynasty, 1368–1644 A.D.), Rhinoceros Horn.

122. "Mist and Trees by the Stream" by Wang Shimin (Qing dynasty, dated 1676 A.D.), Hanging Scroll on Paper.

123. "Streams and Mountains Without End" by Wang Jian (Qing dynasty, dated 1675 A.D.), Hanging Scroll on Paper.

124. "Wild Groves and Rushing Waterfall" by Wang Hui (Qing dynasty, dated 1672 A.D.), Hanging Scroll on Paper.

125. "Landscape in the Manner of Ni Zan and Huang Gongwang" by Wang Yuanqi (Qing dynasty, dated 1710 A.D.), Hanging Scroll on Paper.

黄海松石

為

文翁先生寫 弘仁

128. "Pine and Rocks in the Yellow Sea" by Hongren (Qing dynasty, dated 1660 A.D.), Hanging Scroll on Paper.

129. "Landscape" by Kuncan (Qing dynasty, dated 1661 A.D.), Hanging Scroll on Paper.

130. "Wild Geese Among Rushes" by Zhu Da (Qing dynasty, 1664–1911 A.D.),
    Hanging Scroll on Paper.

132. "Listening to the Spring in a House by the Torrent" by Gong Xian, (Qing dynasty, 1664–1911 A.D.), Hanging Scroll on Silk.

133. "Immortals' Palace in the Spring Mountains" by Yuan Jiang (Qing dynasty, dated 1710 A.D.),
Hanging Scroll on Silk.

135. *"Osmanthus Fragrans* and Tree Pie" by Hua Yan (Qing dynasty, dated 1742 A.D.), Hanging Scroll on Silk.

吾鄉龔御史田居先生家有辛貢粉梅丁處士鈍丁家有王晃紅梅皆元時高流妙筆
今用二老之法畫于一幅中白之朱之恍然置身在水邊林下也葁之冷香伊誰聞之
敬堂先生大雅清賞　　　　　　　　　　七十三翁杭郡金農記

136. "Plum Blossoms" by Jin Nong (Qing dynasty, 1644–1911 A.D.), Hanging Scroll on Silk.

休將水墨為荷寫
污泥墨暈翻
飛色盡墨
夜墨雲翅
淑草堂尺素雨
鳳雲雜正卯
中冬示师北行鏡
下寫花竹面之頂痕
墨汁山房 李鱓

137. "Ink Lotus" by Li Shan (Qing dynasty, dated 1735 A.D.), Hanging Scroll on Paper.

138. "Bamboo and Rocks" by Zheng Xie (Qing dynasty, dated 1759 A.D.), Hanging Scroll on Paper.

139. "Zhong Kui" by Luo Ping (Qing dynasty, 1644–1911 A.D.), Hanging Scroll on Paper.

140. "Loquats" by Xugu (Qing dynasty, dated 1895 A.D.), Hanging Scroll on Paper.

141. "Fisherman" by Ren Yi (Qing dynasty, dated
1892 A.D.), Hanging Scroll on Paper.

144. Porcelain Bowl with *Wucai* Enamels on a Red Ground (Qing
dynasty, Kangxi reign, 1662–1722 A.D.), Jingde Ware.

142. Small Vase, Kidney Bean Red Glaze (Qing dynasty, Kangxi
reign, 1662–1722 A.D.), Jingde Ware.

145. Porcelain Dish with *Fencai* Overglaze Enamel Decoration (Qing dynasty, Yongzheng reign, 1723–1735 A.D.), Jingde Ware.

146. Porcelain Vase with Gold Enamel on Red Ground (Qing dynasty, Daoguang reign, 1821–1850 A.D.), Jingde Ware, "Shende Tang" mark.

147. Vase, Cloisonné Enamel with Openwork Gilt Bronze Panels (Qing dynasty, 1644–1911 A.D.).

153. Pavilion (Qing dynasty, 1644–1911 A.D.), Carved Red Lacquer.

154. Armchair with Design of "Nine Dragons Raging in the Sea"
     (Qing dynasty, 1644–1911 A.D.), Carved Red Lacquer.
155. Round Table with Decoration of Figures and Flowers
     (Qing dynasty, 1644–1911 A.D.), Carved Red Lacquer.

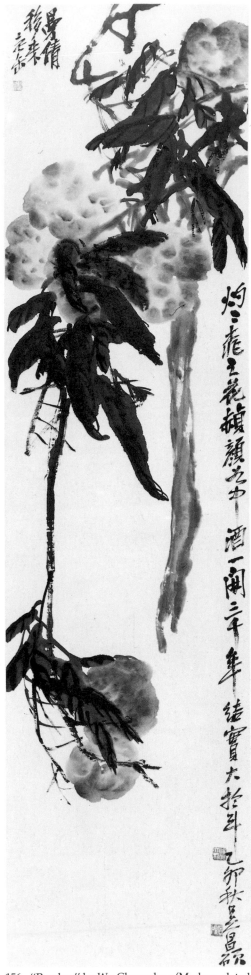

156. "Peaches" by Wu Changshuo (Modern, dated
1915), Hanging Scroll on Paper.

作畫以布置後施
鉤勒研掭水墨暈
彰悉有根概為備
及積之久虎者恆多
宜疎之其藝林研
輕學少有未五年
取龕先生屬 賓虹丙戌
[印] 年八十三

158. "Landscape" by Huang Binhong (Modern, dated 1946), Hanging Scroll on Paper.

159. "Old Cypress" by Xu Beihong (Modern, dated 1934), Hanging Scroll on Paper.

160. "Bald Vulture" by Pan Tianshou (Modern), Hanging Scroll
on Paper.

162. Vase with Carved Birds and Chains (Contemporary, 1911– ), White

161. Basket (Contemporary, 1911– ), Carved Ivory.

63. Openwork Phoenix Plaque (Tang dynasty, 618–907 A.D.), Jade.

150. Brush Pot with Design Illustrating "Welcoming the Wild Goose"
Carved by Wu Zhifan (Early Qing dynasty, 1644–1795 A.D.), Bamboo.

# CATALOG ENTRIES

### 1. *Dou,* Grey Pottery
*Neolithic age, Songze culture (4,950–5,860 years ago)*
*H: 14.3 cm; D (mouth): 22.9 cm*

*Dou* vessels were popular food containers during China's Neolithic age.

This *dou* was excavated in 1976 from the middle stratum at the site of Songze in Qingpu County, Shanghai Municipality, and belongs to the Songze culture.

Its basin-shaped, shallow body rests on a short and thick conical foot with a recessed upper part and a lower part ornamented with five sets of openwork motifs made of rounded triangles and circles and alternating at equal intervals with clusters of prick marks. The workmanship is precise and the shape visually pleasing.

According to radiocarbon tests conducted on human bones from the same stratum, this object dates from 5,860 years ago with a variable of plus or minus 245 years.

### 2. Pig-shaped *Yi,* Grey Pottery
*Neolithic age, Songze culture (4,950–5,860 years ago)*
*H: 6.7 cm; D (mouth): 12.5 cm*

Pottery *yi* were water vessels. Unearthed in 1974 from the middle stratum at the site of Songze in Qingpu County, Shanghai Municipality, this *yi* belongs to the Songze culture.

A sturdy vessel, it has a straight-sided body with squared-off lips and a rounded base. There is a spout on one side of the mouth rim and near the base an impressed circular band of horizontal S-shaped motifs. When the vessel is reversed, the shape of a fat pig becomes apparent. It is as if the "spout" formed the pig's mouth and a piece was added where the spout and the body of the vessel meet to form the snout. To the right and left above this snout are a pair of carved eyes and a pair of applied ears.

This remarkably ingenious vessel is undoubtedly the work of art of a primitive society and a concrete proof that pigs were already domesticated by that time.

According to radiocarbon tests conducted on human bones from the same stratum, this object dates from 5,180 years ago with a variable of plus or minus 140 years.

### 3. *Ding,* Clay Mixed with Fine Sand
*Neolithic age, Songze culture (4,950–5,860 years ago)*
*H: 19.5 cm; D (mouth): 36.2 cm*

*Ding* were cooking vessels made in eastern China during the late part of the Neolithic age.

This vessel was unearthed in 1966 from the lower stratum of the Siqian village site in Qingpu County in Shanghai Municipality. It has the shape of a shallow basin resting on three flattened legs. Its entire body is decorated with u-shaped grooves and the upper part of its legs with a horizontal row of depressed dots, while a straight flange flanked by two incisions runs down the center of each leg.

Judging from its shape and decoration, this vessel belongs to the late phase of the Songze culture. It dates back over 4,950 years.

### 4. Openwork *Hu* Jar with Two Walls, Black Pottery
*Neolithic age, Songze culture (4,950–5,860 years ago)*
*H: 15.5 cm; D (mouth): 8.1 cm*

This *hu* was excavated in 1966 from the lower stratum of the Siqian village site in Qingpu County, Shanghai Municipality. The greyish-white core of its paste is coated with a layer of black slip. The vessel has two walls, an inner and an outer one. The inner body is in the shape of a tubular *hu* with an angular shoulder, and the outer body is decorated in openwork, while the edges of the short neck and the foot are foliated. The openwork decoration that covers the belly and foot consists of circles and rounded triangles with bow-shaped sides and resembles a cluster of flower buds about to burst forth. The shape of this rare and precious work of art of the Songze Neolithic culture is freshly innovative and pleasing to the eye. The vessel dates back over 4,950 years.

### 5. *Hu* of the Shilingxia Type, Painted Pottery
(Colorplate II)
*Neolithic age, Gansu Yangshao culture (approximately 5,000 years ago)*
*H: 27.0 cm; D (mouth): 13.8 cm; D (base): 11.8 cm*

The Shilingxia type of pottery is primarily distributed over the area of Tianshui and Wushan Counties in eastern Gansu Province. It represents vestiges of an ancient culture between the Miaodigou type of the Yangshao culture and the Majiayao type of the Gansu Yangshao culture.

Shilingxia painted pottery is an outgrowth of the Miaodigou type, and much of it is orange or brick red. It is occasionally white slipped, and the painted decor is done primarily in black. Inside painting is rare. Ornamental schemes are comparatively free and clear with animal motifs, including birds and frogs, as well as geometrical motifs, such as linear and wavy patterns and triangular hooked-leaf motifs with bow-shaped sides.

This *hu* has a flaring mouth, a flattened lip, a flat base and a belly completely rounded out. Painted in black over an orange-red body, the decor consists of triangular hooked leaves with bow-shaped sides and bird motifs. The design of this exceptionally fine piece is striking and the brushwork fluid.

### 6. *He* with Lid, Black Pottery
*Neolithic age, Liangzhu culture (3,920–4,710 years ago)*
*H (including lid): 16.1 cm; D (mouth, crosswise): 5.45 cm; D (mouth, lengthwise): 5.95 cm*

Pottery *he* were used during China's Neolithic age for heating and boiling liquids. Their form developed from a strange *ding* of the Songze culture in the shape of a duck's belly.

This elegant *he* was unearthed in 1961 from a grave in the lower stratum at the Guangfulin site in Songjiang County in Shanghai Municipality and is one of the typical vessels of the Liangzhu culture. Its mouth is oval, spouted and fitted with a lid, which is perforated with two small holes for stringing. The belly is also oval, and the vessel has a back handle. It rests on three pillar-like legs and it dates back over 4,200 years.

### 7. *Gui,* Red Pottery (Colorplate III)
*Neolithic age, Liangzhu culture (3,920–4,710 years ago)*
*H: 24.0 cm*

Pottery *gui* were used during the late Neolithic age in eastern China for heating and boiling liquids. The shape evolved from an unusual Songze *gui* with two lobed legs and a handle.[1]

One of the typical vessels of the Liangzhu culture, this *gui* was unearthed in 1972 from the lower stratum of the Tinglin site in Jinshan County in Shanghai Municipality. One side of the mouth was pinched to form a spout, the body rests on three pouch-shaped, hollow legs and its back is equipped with a semicircular handle. The whole vessel was made of clay mixed with fine sand, and its shape is extraordinary.

According to radiocarbon tests made on charcoal found

in the same stratum, this *gui* dates back 4,200 years, with a variable of plus or minus 145 years.

(1) Zhejiang Provincial Museum, " 河姆渡遗址第一期发掘报告 " ("Hemudu yizhi diyi qi fajue baogao", "Report on the First Season of Excavations at the Site of Hemudu"), *Kaogu Xuebao*, 1978, no. 1, pp. 39–93.

## 8. Animal Mask Pendant, Jade
*Neolithic age, Liangzhu culture (about 3,920–4,710 years ago)*
*H: 2.8 cm; W: 4.0 cm*

This semicircular piece of ornament in the shape of an animal mask is carved[1] from grey-green jade. Cut in low relief, the mask has large eyes and a wide mouth. It looks stern and mysterious. Characterized by meticulous, well-rounded and straightforward workmanship, it is a rare and beautiful piece of jade from the Neolithic period. There is an oval aperture on the upper part of the ornament and two small round holes on the bottom part, obviously for stringing.

Similar pieces have been excavated in recent years from sites such as Sidun[2] of Wujin County in Jiangsu Province, Mt. Zhangling in Wu County and Zanmiao in Jiangning County.

(1) The Chinese terms "cut and polish" are more accurate than our own term "carve."
(2) Nanjing Museum, "江苏武进寺墩遗址的试掘" ("Jiangsu Wujin Sidun yizhi di shijue", "Trial Digging of a Neolithic Site at Sidun, Wujin, Jiangsu"), *Kaogu*, 1981, no. 3, fig. 7, p. 197.

## 9. *Cong*, Jade (Colorplate I)
*Neolithic age, Liangzhu culture (about 3,920–4,710 years ago)*
*H: 39.3 cm; W (top): 8.1 cm; W (bottom): 7.1 cm; D (hole): 5.0 cm*

Carved in green jade with patches of dark brown, this *cong* is shaped like a tall cylinder inside a rectangle and tapers toward the base. A central perforation runs the entire length of the object, which is divided into 15 sections. Each section is incised with two circles and alternating long and short lines arranged symmetrically on either side of the corner line. This is a linear rendering of a symbolic animal mask. The incised lines are powerfully carved and arranged in an orderly manner. There is also a feather design incised below the upper mouth rim.

The *Dazongbo* section in the *Chunguan* chapter of the *Zhouli*[1] states: "Green *bi* [is used in] worshipping Heaven, yellow *cong* [in] worshipping Earth." The *cong* was already associated with the religious activities of the Neolithic period as a ritual object. In recent years such pieces have been unearthed from Neolithic burials at Mt. Caoxie and Mt. Zhangling, Wu County, and Sidun of Wujin Conty, Jiangsu Province, as well as in Zhejiang and Anhui Provinces. All are characteristic of the Liangzhu culture.

(1) *The Book of Rites,* an ancient work of uncertain date, describes the services of the officials of the Zhou (ca. 1027–222 B.C.) court.

## 10. Ceremonial Blade, Jade
*Neolithic age*
*L: 29.3 cm; W: 7.0 cm*

The texture of this jade blade is smooth and shiny with patches of green in various shades. Oblong in shape, it has a level and straight back with a row of three small perforations. The cutting edge is slightly longer than the back and is sharpened from both sides. One of the narrow ends is also sharp, while the other has a round perforation. Judg-ing from the two sharp edges, it may well be that the blade was used both horizontally and vertically. In the Neolithic period, the techniques of drilling holes and polishing had already reached a high level of maturity.

Other jade tools of the late Neolithic period have been excavated from Henan, Hebei, Shaanxi and Shandong.

## 11. Duck-shaped *Hu*, Stoneware with Impressed Design
(Colorplate IV)
*Shang dynasty (16th–11th century B.C.)*
*H: 10.0 cm; D (mouth): 7.2 cm*

Impressed stonewares form an important category of the ceramics made in southeastern China during the Shang and Zhou cultures. The name derives from the geometric designs that were impressed on the surfaces of the vessels.

This *hu* was found in 1960 in the middle stratum of the Maqiao site in Shanghai County in Shanghai Municipality. Its purplish, dark brown clay is very hard, and it is covered with a thin layer of dark brown glaze. The vessel has a tall neck and a flattened belly, with one side shaped to resemble a duck's tail, surmounted by a handle. It rests on a conical foot, and the belly is decorated with an impressed rope pattern. This *hu* looks just like a duck standing still. It is a true picture of the numerous aquatic birds that haunt the waters of Lake Taihu.

According to thermoluminescence tests made on sherds from the same stratum, this vessel dates back to 3,250 years ago, with a time span variable of ten percent.

## 12. *Gu*, Black Pottery
*Shang dynasty (16th–11th century B.C.)*
*H: 24.0 cm; D (mouth): 9.4 cm*

The *gu* is one of the popular wine vessels of the Shang dynasty. This specimen was unearthed in 1960 from the middle stratum of the Maqiao site in Shanghai County. The off-white core of the paste is coated with a layer of black slip, a building method inherited from the Liangzhu culture.[1] However, with its elongated body, its trumpet mouth, flat base and waistband decorated with three bow-strings in relief, this vessel is closely related in shape to the Erlitou culture in Henan. It may reflect the cultural exchanges prevailing during the Shang dynasty between the Central Plain and the Jiangsu-Zhejiang region.

According to thermoluminescence tests conducted on sherds from the same stratum, the vessel dates back 3,250 years, with a ten percent variable.

(1) See Catalogue no. 6.

## 13. *Li* with Animal Masks, Bronze
*Shang dynasty, Erligang phase (16th–14th century B.C.)*
*H: 19.2 cm; D: 14.6 cm*

The animal masks on the lobed legs of this *li* have bulging eyes, and the neck is decorated with nondescript animal shapes. The design is rather coarse. The main decorative motifs are framed by rows of circles, a feature which is common to many such ornamental schemes and characteristic of Erligang designs. One handle and leg of the vessel are in line with one another, but the other handle is simply placed directly opposite the first on the mouth rim and is not lined up with either of the other two legs.

A number of bronze *li* vessels belonging to the Erligang phase have been excavated. They are similar in shape to this one, but the decor of this vessel is the most ostentatious. This sort of decoration, covering the entire surface of the vessel, is particular to bronze vessels of the late period of the Erligang phase.

The Erligang culture of the Shang dynasty was first discovered in 1952 at Erligang, in Zhengzhou. This is an early Shang culture that predates the Yinxu period.[1] The precise stratigraphy of the Zhengzhou excavations has established its relative dating, as the Erligang culture is there overlaid by a stratum typical of the Yinxu period. The Erligang culture is, therefore, prior in date to the 14th century B.C. move by King Pangeng to Yin. Remains of this culture have not only been discovered with relative frequency in northern China, but have also repeatedly been found in the middle and lower reaches of the Yangzi.

The repertory of the Erligang bronze casting industry was already fairly broad. Excavated examples include food vessels, cooking vessels, water containers and numerous other types, already constituting an assortment of ritual vessels.

(1) Yinxu, literally "Wastes of the Yin." Yin designates the latter part of the Shang dynasty. The terms "Yinxu period" and "Anyang period" are synonymous.

**14.** *Jue* **with Animal Masks, Bronze** (Colorplate V)
*Shang dynasty, Erligang phase (16th–14th century B.C.)*
*H: 14.6 cm; L (from spout to tail): 15.4 cm*

The mouth of this *jue* is equipped with a long, narrow spout to pour wine and other liquids and a tail tapering to a point. Two short uprights are attached close to the spout. The flattened body is oval in section, the bottom flat, and three curved, awl-shaped legs are attached to the base. This type of *jue* with flattened body is one of the earliest forms of the vessel. Its waist is decorated with deeply carved, broad animal masks. *Gu* and *jue* vessels form the most basic group of ritual bronze wine vessels excavated in Shang dynasty burials.

**15.** *Jia* **with Animal Mask, Bronze**
*Shang dynasty, Erligang phase (16th–14th century B.C.)*
*H: 35.2 cm; D: 18.2 cm*

The *jia* is a libation vessel to pour out wine during sacrifices and as a drinking vessel for wine at banquets. This particular vessel has a flaring mouth and a high neck with a pair of capped uprights on the front edge of the mouth rim. The neck and body form separate sections, the bottom is flat and the base is equipped with three hollow, bludgeon-shaped legs, triangular in section and communicating with the bottom of the vessel. The neck and body are both decorated with animal masks whose structure is already relatively complex, as one would expect from a vessel cast fairly late in the Erligang phase.

The *jia* shape emerged very early. Ceramic *jia* vessels have been discovered at Longshan culture and Erlitou culture sites. Bronze *jia* vessels were already current during the Erligang phase.

**16.** *Zun* **Inscribed** 㕑 **, Bronze**
*Shang dynasty, middle Anyang phase*
*(13th–12th century B.C.)*
*H: 34.8 cm; D (mouth): 32.7 cm; D (foot): 18.8 cm*
*Gift of Mr. Ye Shuzhong*

This *zun* has a widely flaring mouth, broad shoulders and a high conical foot. The neck and the foot are each decorated with three bowstrings. The animal masks on the shoulder are enhanced by three bovine heads in the round, and the body is adorned with three large animal masks. The design is structured in such a way that the principal and background motifs are not clearly differentiated; they are all made of a close-knit meander pattern.[1] This type of fine, skillful decoration is special to the middle Anyang phase, distinguishing it from the plain, broad style of the Erligang and early Anyang phases. The earliest *zun* vessels are broad-shouldered with widely flaring mouth rims. Broad-shouldered *zun* vessels are already seen at Erligang, but by the later Anyang phase of the Shang culture, this shape

was no longer fashionable. There are three cruciform perforations on the foot; their important function is to help remove the air and humidity from within the foot. The inscription 㕑,[2] which is the clan name of the maker of the vessel, is located at the bottom of the vessel.

(1) "Thunder pattern" in the Chinese text.
(2) The transcription of this graph is still under study.

**17.** *Ding,* **Inscribed** 㠭 **, Bronze**
*Shang dynasty, late Anyang phase (12th–11th century B.C.)*
*H: 20.8 cm; D (mouth): 16.4 cm*
*Gift of Mr. Wu Qingyi*

The earliest extant bronze *ding* with flat legs belong to the Erligang phase. These legs were just three oblique, thin supporting slabs, which do not command attention. The legs of this *ding*, however, are shaped like birds whose claws and hanging tails are the points of support and whose heads carry the body of the *ding*, turning a utilitarian object into an outstanding work of art. The body is encircled with a row of cicadas.

This refined type of *ding* was not intended to be used over a fire as a cooking vessel, since if such highly decorative feet were exposed to high temperatures, the tin contained in the bronze alloy would melt. There are a number of excavated bronze *ding* vessels that are self-named "food *ding*." They were used to deposit cooked meats. This *ding* belongs to this category of containers.

The wall of the body of the vessel has a three-graph inscription reading " 㠭 Fu Ding",[1] meaning that it was a sacrificial vessel made by 㠭 for Father Ding.

(1) The transcription of this graph is still under study.

**18.** *Gui,* **Inscribed** *You Fu Kui,* **Bronze**
*Shang dynasty, late Anyang phase (12th–11th century B.C.)*
*H: 17.4 cm; D (mouth): 23.5 cm; D (base): 19.6 cm*
*Gift of Mr. Wu Qingyi*

*Gui* vessels form a large category of bronze food vessels and were used for several species of millet, rice and other foodstuffs.

This *gui* is relatively large and is decorated on its belly with a "nipple-and-thunder" pattern.[1] The neck and the foot have "long-nosed dragons"[2] whose bodies are relatively small, about the same length as the long noses. This is a variant of the "curled-nose animal" pattern. This type of decor is fairly common, with the long-nosed dragon decor of this *gui* being the latest in date. The top parts of the handles on either side of the vessel are adorned with large animal heads. These rather large handles are of a type relatively early among bronze *gui* handles. They first appeared at the site of Panlongcheng, Huangpi, Hubei, on bronze *gui* vessels corresponding to the Erligang phase of the Shang dynasty and then disappeared for a rather long period of time, as most of the *gui* vessels from the mid Anyang phase lack handles.[3] Double-handled *gui* reappear in the late Anyang phase. The handles of this vessel have spurs,[4] which are characteristic of the late Anyang type. On the bottom of the vessel, a three-graph inscription reads, *You Fu Kui,* meaning that this vessel was made by the You family for Father Kui.[5]

(1) More commonly and less picturesquely known in English terminology as "compound lozenges."
(2) More commonly known in English terminology as "trunked dragons."
(3) Such handleless *gui* are also known as *yü.*
(4) "Ear ornaments" in the Chinese text.
(5) 酉父癸.

**19.** *Gong,*[1] **Inscribed** 兴 *Fu Yi,* **Bronze** (Colorplate VIII)

*Shang dynasty, late Anyang phase (12th–11th century B.C.)*
*H: 29.5 cm; L: 31.5 cm*

This category of vessels is not self-named; the appellation *gong* was set by modern archaeologists.

The rhino-tusk shaped wine vessel from Shilou, Shanxi,[2] with its dragon-shaped extremity and its cover, is the prototype of the *gong* shape. Our *gong* and other similar ones which have a large animal head up front must have evolved from the rhino-tusk shaped *gong* to take on a form more suitable to containers. This category of vessels has, without exception, a cover in the shape of an animal head, which can be that of an ox, a sheep or another real animal, or again, as in the case of this vessel, that of an imaginary animal. A dragon in low relief with a long body and curled tail is placed between the two horns, while the back part of the cover is in the form on an oxhead. A large phoenix decorates each side of the body. The claws of these phoenixes extend down to the foot, thus putting its stature in evidence. The phoenixes that decorate the foot have long, curling tails.

While the *gong* category of wine containers belongs mainly to the later Shang dynasty, a small number of them were still cast during the early and middle Western Zhou dynasty. Late specimens, however, were no longer made as wine containers. By that time they had become basins for ablutions.

The vessel's cover has the three-graph inscription, 兴 *Fu Yi*.[3] It was a sacrificial vessel made by the 兴 family for their Father Yi.

(1)  舢 Traditionally pronounced *guang*.
(2)  Excavated in 1959. See William Watson, *The Genius of China*, London 1973, Fig. 82.
(3)  The transcription of this graph is still under study.

## 20.  Square *Yue* Axe with Cruciform Motifs, Bronze
(Colorplate VII)
*Shang dynasty, late Anyang phase (12th–11th century B.C.)*
*L: 35.6 cm; W: 33.2 cm (maximum)*

This is the only extant square *yue* axe inlaid with cruciform motifs. Its peculiarity rests with its blade, which is square and flat. In the majority of such pieces, the blade is wider than the butt, while in this axe the blade and the butt have about the same dimensions.

The *yue* is a large axe which was popular during the Shang dynasty. According to the *Wangzhi* section of the *Liji*,[1] "The feudal princes are given bows and arrows to attack; they are given axes to kill"—a passage that shows that the *yue* was meant to kill. In bronze inscriptions the image of a *yue* shown chopping off a head served as a clan emblem. Large *yue* have been excavated from Fuhao's tomb at Xiaotun, Anyang, in Henan Province,[2] and from the great tomb at Yidu, Shandong.[3]

This *yue* axe weighs five kilograms. Such an oversized, overweighted weapon must have been unwieldy. As it is moreover inlaid with turquoise stone, it could not have been used to kill people, rather to reveal the social status of its owner. The bronze inscriptions of the Western Zhou record royal gifts of bronze *yue* axes to high officials. All these gifts served as a means of bestowing military power. Judging from the form of the written graph for axe in bronze inscriptions, the *yue* originally had a handle with a curled extremity and three square holes on the butt to allow the handle to be tied up with a leather strap. The handle of this *yue* must have been 3.5 cm in width.

(1)  *Liji* was compiled in the Western Han. It records the discussions of Confucius and his disciples on ritual and a code of ethics. The *Wangzhi* section, the *Royal Commands*, deals with the behavior appropriate to the ruler.
(2)  Chinese Academy of Social Sciences, Archaeological Re-

search Institute, 殷墟妇好墓 (*Yinxu Fuhao Mu, The Tomb of Fuhao at Yinxu*), Beijing, Wenwu Press, 1980, Color Plate 3.
(3)  Shandong Provincial Museum, "山东益都苏埠屯第一号奴隶殉葬墓" ("Shandong Yidu Sufoutun diyi hao nuli xunzangmu", "Slave Satellite Tomb No. 1 at Sufoutun, Yidu, Shandong"), *Wenwu*, 1972, no. 8, fig. 28, p. 29.

## 21.  *You*-shaped Vessel, Inscribed 八 , Bronze
*Shang dynasty, late Anyang phase (12th–11th century B.C.)*
*H: 23.8 cm; D (mouth): 15.2 cm*

This type of vessel looks like the *you*,[1] but its large, flaring mouth is very different from that of the usual *you*. The body of the vessel is round with a circular base and a handle made to resemble a rope, at each end of which is a lunar toad.

Most bronze vessels decorated with lunar toads are water vessels. In Chinese mythology, the moon spirit has the form of a toad, the moon looks like water and the sun looks like fire. It is therefore possible that this type of *you*-shaped container decorated with lunar toads was a water vessel.

We know also of one *pou* and one *dou* with toad decoration. The former is in the Asian Art Museum of San Francisco, and the latter, excavated at Lanjiagou, Shilou, Shanxi Province, has handles decorated with toads and snakes. A *you*, similar to ours but with a foot, is also in the collection of the Asian Art Museum of San Francisco. Another one without the toads is said to have been in the Huc M. Luguiens collection in Honolulu. In 1976, a vessel was excavated from Fuhao's tomb at Anyang, Henan, with the same shape as this *you* and with Fuhao's name cast inside the body.

This *you* bucket has the graph 八 cast on the outside of the body. This is the same clan name as that inscribed on the *zun* illustrated in Figure 16. Bronze vessels inscribed with this clan name are numerous, as the clan was one of the great families during the period from the middle Shang through the early Western Zhou.

(1)  See Colorplate IX.

## 22.  Notched *Xuanji*[1] Disc, Agate
*Shang dynasty, (16th–11th century B.C.)*
*D: 10.3 cm*

This circular piece carved from agate is pure, white and without any blemishes. On the edge are carved three notches, each with a small flange. This piece is done with great precision.

This type of jade has been discovered in archaeological excavations of the past few years, e.g., the Neolithic burial site of Sanlihe in Jiao County, Shandong Province, and Fuhao's tomb[2] at Yinxu, Anyang. This example is similar to the one unearthed from Fuhao's tomb.

(1)  An astronomical instrument used for watching the stars.
(2)  See Catalogue no. 20, footnote (2).

## 23.  Ceremonial Axe, Jade
*Late Shang dynasty (14th–11th century B.C.)*
*L: 14.2 cm; W: 9.3 cm*

Ceremonial jade axes of that period were derived from stone tools. This one is carved from white jade. Its shape is perfect, and it displays symmetrical projections on two sides. A circular perforation was drilled into the tang, and the blade is crescent-shaped. The entire piece is without surface decoration. Polished to a sheen, it is simple and straightforward.

## 24.  *Ge* Dagger with Animal Mask, Jade (Colorplate VI)
*Late Shang dynasty (14th–11th century B.C.)*
*L: 25.3 cm; W: 5.8 cm*

Bluish green in color, this jade *ge* has sharp cutting edges. Precise and highly decorative animal masks are carved in raised lines and low relief on both sides of the upper parts of the tang and blade. The central ridge of the blade is decorated with three straight raised lines. This type of jade weapon was used as an insignia of rank.

## 25. *Ding*, Inscribed *De*,[1] Bronze (Colorplate X)
*Western Zhou period, reign of King Cheng*
*(11th–10th century B.C.)*
*H: 78.0 cm; D (mouth): 56.0 cm*
*Gift of Messrs. Wang Jingzhi and Chen Xiangjiu*

This monumental *ding* is one of a small number of large *ding* vessels surviving from the Western Zhou period and one of the even smaller number of such vessels discovered so far that date back to the early phase of the period. However, at the time all these vessels were very important.

Below the mouth rim of this *ding* there is a band of animal masks flanked by dragon motifs on either side. U-shaped depressions, 7.5 cm deep, mark the point where the legs join the body of the vessel. During the Western Zhou, the legs of large *ding* vessels were usually made in this way in order to prevent the joints between legs and body from splitting as a result of excessive pressure during the cooling process of casting.

There are four extant bronze vessels made by De, and this piece is the largest of the group. The *De square ding* is also in the collection of the Shanghai Museum and bears an inscription indicating that De was a contemporary of King Cheng. An 11-graph inscription is cast on the inside wall of this vessel. It records that De received a gift of 20 strings of cowrie shells from the Zhou king, whereupon De made this ritual vessel. This was a most generous gift, since at the time cowrie shells were a precious commodity. The nobles of the Western Zhou period often inscribed acts of royal favor on bronze vessels as a way of showing off their high standing.

(1)  德.

## 26. Square *Ding*, Inscribed *Huo Fu Kui*, Bronze
*Early Western Zhou period (11th–10th century B.C.)*
*H: 27.3 cm; Mouth rim: 16.1 × 20.6 cm*

This square *ding* is really rectangular. It is decorated with animal masks on the body and double-bodied dragons below the mouth rim. The dragons' heads are placed in the middle, and their twisting bodies unfold on either side. The legs of the vessel bear banana leaf motifs.[1]

The earliest square *ding* vessels are the ceramic examples seen in the Erlitou culture[2] and bronzes from the Erligang phase of the Shang dynasty. All of these are nearly square, while the rectangular shape first appears during the Anyang period. The special graph for square *ding* was 鼐, which is made of paired elements. The large square *ding* vessels excavated at Erligang, Zhengzhou, form a pair, with a small difference in heights. Another pair of square *ding* vessels, one decorated with an ox and the other with a deer, came from an earlier discovery in Tomb 1001 at Houjiazhuang, Anyang, where they were found side by side. The two large square *ding* vessels unearthed from Fuhao's tomb at Anyang in 1976 were of similar shapes and dimensions. In addition, the tomb contained two rectangular *ding* vessels with flattened legs, also of identical shape and size. This *Huo Fu Kui fang ding* is also one of a pair. On the inside wall a six-character inscription reads: "Sacrificial vessel made by the Huo (family) for (their) Father Kui."[3]

(1)  More commonly known in English terminology as "hanging blades" or "cicada hanging blades."
(2)  The Loyang Excavation Team, Institute of Archaeology, Academia Sinica, "河南偃师二里头遗址发掘简报" ("Henan

Yanshi Erlitou yizhi fajue jianbao", "Brief Report on the Excavations at the Site at Erlitou, Yenshi, Henan"), *Kaogu*, 1965, no. 5, Plate 2, fig. 3.
(3)  作父癸尊彝或.

## 27. *Gui*, Inscribed *E Shu*, Bronze
*Early Western Zhou period (11th–10th century B.C.)*
*H: 18.7 cm; D (mouth): 18.2 cm; Base: 14.5 × 14.7 cm*

This four-handled *gui* has a shallow body cast onto a square base. Its mouth rim is decorated with coiled dragons and whorl circles, its high cylindrical foot with animal masks and the four sides of the square base with long-crested birds. There is an inscription on the inside bottom recording that the owner of the vessel was named E Shu.

There are two possible locations for E. One, Qinyang in the Yellow River basin, was the state of E during the Shang dynasty and into the Western Zhou. The second, in the Yangzi basin north of the Han River and west of the Huai, was the state of E during the Western Zhou. A *zun* vessel belonging to the younger brother of the Marquis of E was excavated at Anju, Sui County in Hubei Province. The characteristics of the basic copper carbonate[1] present in the oxidized surface[2] of the *E Shu gui* differ from that of the younger brother of the Marquis of E and are typical of the Yellow River basin. Therefore, the *E Shu gui*[3] came from the E State in Qinyang.

There is a bell within the square base of this *gui*, which, when shaken, emits a clear, penetrating tone. The making of bronze vessels incorporating bells goes back to the Shang dynasty, as shown by the *gu* vessel with a bell that was excavated at Shilouzhen, Lüliang County, Shanxi Province.

(1)  Which is contained in the malachite or azurite that is part of the bronze patina.
(2)  Or patina.
(3)  鄂叔簋.

## 28. *You* with Chevrons of Square Meanders, Bronze (Colorplate IX)
*Early Western Zhou period (11th–10th century B.C.)*
*H: 25.0 cm; D (mouth): 13.8 cm; D (base): 16.8 cm*

This squat, pot-bellied vessel is entirely decorated with an elegant pattern of chevrons of thick square meanders[1] alternating with thin ones. This pattern is very seldom seen on Western Zhou bronze vessels. The cover and the bottom of the vessel are inscribed, respectively, with four graphs which read: "Precious vessel made for the ancestral temple." The inscription does not give the name of the maker.

The majority of *you* vessels are oval in shape with a handle, whereas this one has a round body, a type not too often seen. It is the archaeologists of the Song dynasty who gave the name *you* to this category of vessels; no self-named *you* has been discovered so far. Very few *you* were made during the early and middle phases of the Anyang period when tall and flattened *hu* vessels were popular, and they gradually disappeared during the mid-Western Zhou after the appearance of tall *hu* vessels with square mouths and round bodies. The period of greatest popularity for the *you* was during the latest phase of the Shang occupation of the Anyang site and during the early Western Zhou. Its function was the same as that of the *hu*, both being important wine containers.

(1)  Catalogue no. 16, footnote (1).

## 29. Square *Zun*, Inscribed *Kui Gu*, Bronze
*Early Western Zhou period (11th–10th century B.C.)*
*H: 21.8 cm; D (mouth): 20.1 cm; Base: 11.8 × 12.3 cm*

This *zun* has a round mouth, a square body and an angular shoulder. The *zun* with a broad, angular shoulder originated during the Erligang phase of the Shang dynasty, when the conical foot of the vessel was perforated with square or small holes, and lasted until the middle of the Anyang phase, after which time it lost popularity. Examples of *zun* with narrow, angular shoulders continue to be seen into the early Western Zhou, but their conical feet are no longer perforated by holes.

Dating to the period overlapping the end of the Shang and the beginning of the Zhou dynasties, this piece is the latest manifestation of the *zun* with an angular shoulder. The neck is decorated with banana leaves[1] and animal masks, the shoulder with dragons, the belly with large animal masks, the foot band with birds. Each of the four corners of the vessel bears an elephant head with spiraling horns. These heads were made separately after the completion of the vessel itself, which was cast with tenons sticking out at each of the four corners; then small molds were built up for the casting of the heads. This is why these heads overlap the shoulder decoration. The shape is perfect. The fine meander pattern was incised with such meticulousness that it can be said: "Each thread was done with care."

On the bottom of the vessel a four-graph inscription reads: "Kui Gu made this sacrificial vessel."[2] Kui Gu was the name of the owner of the vessel. In Shang times the Kui territory was the area which today is located northwest of Boai in Henan and is contiguous to Shanxi Province.

(1) See Catalogue no. 26, footnote (1).
(2) 殷古乍旅 .

### 30. *Zhi*, Inscribed *Fu Geng*, Bronze
*Early Western Zhou period (11th–10th century B.C.)*
*H:14.9 cm; D (mouth): 7.6 cm; D (foot): 5.1 cm*

This small vessel has a flaring mouth, a constricted waist and a low belly. The neck is decorated with banana leaf designs and birds with bifurcated tails. On the body there are large phoenixes with drooping tails. The entire vessel is lightly oxidized, and part of the surface still retains the original bright gold lustre of bronze. The inscription *Fu Geng* inside the bottom of the vessel is the name of the person to whom the vessel was dedicated. The name of the maker is not mentioned.

The *zhi* was used for wine drinking, and this kind of *zhi* first appeared in the late Anyang phase of the Shang dynasty. By the Chunqiu period, there were similar but taller vessels self-named *zhuan*.[1]

(1) 鍴 or 耑 .

### 31. Square *Lei*, Inscribed *Fu Ding*,[1] Bronze
*Early Western Zhou period (11th–10th century B.C.)*
*H: 46.4 cm; Mouth: 12.0 × 14.0 cm; Base: 13.7 × 15.1 cm*

This *lei* is a large wine container with a high neck, sloping shoulders and a high foot. The two lateral handles are equipped with rings, and there is also a frontal handle on the lower half of the body. Animal masks flanked by whorl circles decorate the shoulder and the lid. In addition to pairs of eyes, the decor on the mouth rim and foot consists of variations of the animal mask motif, done in extremely fine lines. On the foot these motifs are capped by a ribbon of tall, vertical feather motifs. During the early period of the Anyang phase, these motifs were relatively tall, but at the end of the Shang and beginning of the Zhou periods, they gradually shortened to look like a series of little banners.

(1) 父丁 .

### 32. Square *Yi*, Inscribed *Shi Ju*,[1] Bronze (Colorplate XI)
*Western Zhou period, reign of King Yi*
*(10th–9th century B.C.)*
*H:16.4 cm; Rim: 7.6 × 9.8 cm; Base: 7.5 × 9.6 cm*
*Gift of Mr. Ding Xierou*

This square *yi* has elephant-trunk handles on either side, and the inside is divided into two cubicles by a medial wall. On either side of this wall the cover is perforated with two small square holes to accommodate small wine dippers. The cover and the body of the vessel are decorated with variations of the animal mask pattern, and below the rim and around the foot with variations of animal shapes. This is the ultimate phase in the development of the animal mask motif of the Shang and Zhou dynasties.

The vessel and its lid both bear a 66-graph inscription, the main intent of which is to record a banquet that King Yi held in the inner pavilion of the Kang Palace. Shi Ju presented the King with gifts to enhance the happy occasion, and the King in return ordered his steward to bestow on Shi Ju several jade objects, including a *xi* tablet[2] and a *yuan* sceptre.[3]

(1) 师遽 .
(2) 珛 . The exact shape of this particular object remains to be determined.
(3) 瑗 . A round, perforated disc of jade with a relatively larger hole than a *bi* disc. For *bi* see Catalogue no. 49.

### 33. *Zun* with Dragon Handles, Bronze (Colorplate XII)
*Late Western Zhou period (9th century–771 B.C.)*
*H: 39.1 cm; D: (mouth) 35.4 cm; D: (base) 32.2 cm*

This is a relatively large *zun* vessel, with thick walls, a large mouth, broad shoulders and a body covered with broad, deeply cut grooves.[1] On the side of the vessel, two large vertical dragons of unusual vitality serve as handles. The vessel and the dragon handles were cast separately. Holes were left on the body of the vessel, and the separate pieces were firmly joined with molten bronze, which formed lumpy joint marks clearly visible inside the vessel.

This vessel and its twin were excavated in northern Anhui. The exact place of their discovery is not certain, but according to historical records, northern Anhui was the area where the Huai Yi[2] used to live, so it is possible that this bronze was a Huai Yi vessel of the Western Zhou period.

(1) This type of decoration is better known in standard English terminology as "horizontal ribbing."
(2) Minority tribes living at the confluence of the Huai and Yi Rivers

### 34. *Ling*, Inscribed *Fu Zhong Yi*, Bronze
*Late Western Zhou period (9th century–771 B.C.)*
*H: 44 cm; D (mouth):15.4 cm; D (base):16.9 cm*

This vessel and the large Ke *ding* were excavated in 1890 from a cellar in Ren village, Famen temple in Fufeng County in Shaanxi Province.[1] A rather rare shape in the Mid and Late Western Zhou, the *ling* is a large wine container with a small mouth, broad shoulder and flat bottom, which resembles a ring foot but is, in fact, flat. The cover is very tall and slips far down inside the neck of the vessel. Generally speaking, the *ling* looks like the early Western Zhou *lei*[2] but without handles. The two curled dragons on the shoulders are decorative and unlike the *lei*, this vessel does not have another handle on the lower part of the body. The shoulder and false ring foot are decorated with scale bands running in opposite directions, and from the shoulder down the body is filled with rows of scales, an ornamental scheme that appeared at the end of the early Western Zhou and was popular in the middle and later Western Zhou.

Inscriptions are cast on the vessel's shoulder and the outer rim of the cover—not the inside of the mouth—in order to make them more immediately apparent. The habit of casting inscriptions on the surface of vessels probably originated around this period.

Apparently there are two groups of *ding* made for Father Zhong Yi. In addition, eight bells made for Zhong Yi[3] were excavated in 1960 at Qijiacun, Fufeng County, Shaanxi Province, and it could be that the two Zhong Yi were one and the same person.

(1)  Shanghai Museum, 上海博物馆藏青铜器(*Shanghai Bowuguan cang qingtongqi, Bronze Vessels in the Collection of the Shanghai Museum*), Shanghai, Shanghai Museum, 1964, Plate 47.
(2)  See Figure 31.
(3)  Archaeological Research Institute, Shaanxi Province, *et al*, 陕西出土商周青铜器 (*Shaanxi chutu Shang Zhou qingtongqi, Shang and Zhou Bronze Vessels Unearthed in Shaanxi*), Beijing, Wenwu Press, 1980, vol. 2, Plates 142–149.

### 35.  Large *Zhong* Bell with Dragon Decor, Bronze
*Late Western Zhou period (9th century–771 B.C.)*
*H: 105.0 cm; Shoulder: 29.8 × 38.2 cm; Bottom: 33.3 × 44.0 cm; Length of bottom curved side: 67.5 cm*

This *zhong* bell is thick, heavy and very large. The handle and the body of the bell are decorated with broad, curled dragon motifs in a wide variety of shapes and with particularly long studs.

Tuning percussion bells into a certain musical scale is a peculiarity of the Chinese Bronze culture. This type of large tuned bell produces loud, clear and melodious tones and may have been played in harmony. In 1978, a set of 65 bells was excavated from the Early Warring States tomb of Zheng Hou Yi in Sui County, Hubei. In this set, the large bells were all placed on the bottom level of the bell rack and struck with a large wooden rod to make them chime.

This great bell with dragon decor belongs to the Late Western Zhou period, and it, too, could only be played as a percussion instrument. Together with this group of large bells, there must have been other sets of scaled bells, which explains that, by the late phase of the Western Zhou period, there were already quite a number of complete sets of such bells.

### 36.  *Bo* Bell with Four Tigers, Bronze
*Late Western Zhou period (9th century–771 B.C.)*
*H: 42.0 cm; Shoulder: 12.6 × 17.9 cm;*
*Bottom: 20.7 × 26.4 cm*

Both the back and front of this *bo* bell have a bird-shaped flange, and there are four tigers on the sides. A handle is mounted on the top. On the body of the bell the usual studs have been replaced by symmetrical curled dragons. The piece is relatively large with a flat mouth and is roughly a rounded-off square in shape.

This kind of musical instrument is structurally different from usual bells. Their walls are relatively thin, and their toll is short and monotone. *Bo* bells were used in a different manner than the bells grouped in sets, but they may still have been percussive instruments.

The way in which *bo* bells were combined is not quite clear. The two four-tiger *bo* in the Shanghai Museum form a pair. The *bo* bell set of the Duke of Qin, excavated at Baoji, Shaanxi Province, is composed of three bells, but is far from being a complete set.

### 37.  *Gui*, Grey Pottery
*Western Zhou period (ca. 11th century–771 B.C.)*
*H: 14.5 cm; D (mouth): 19.5 cm*

The *gui* is a food container of ancient China. This bowl was unearthed in 1966 from the middle stratum of the Si-qian village site in Qingpu County in Shanghai Municipality. Its distinctive features are a flat mouth rim, a deep body and a trumpet foot. The decoration on the body consists of five rows of circles and grooves.

This shape is close to that of a Western Zhou pottery *gui* excavated in the Central Plain.[1]

(1)  Not yet published.

### 38.  Pendant with Bird Design, Jade
*Western Zhou period (11th century–771 B.C.)*
*L: 8.3 cm; W: 2.0 cm*

A bird motif is carved in continuous low relief on both sides of this grey-green jade ornament. The fluid and natural linear carving creates a lively image. On one end is a hole drilled from both sides so it can be strung and used as a pendant.

### 39.  *Yi*, Inscribed *Marquis of Qi*,[1] Bronze (Colorplate XIII)
*Early Chunqiu period (770–second half of 6th century B.C.)*
*H: 24.7 cm; L (overall): 48.1 cm*
*Gift of Mr. Shen Tongyue and others*

This is the largest *yi* bronze vessel in existence. Qi was a large state during the Chungqiu period, and the vessel is a manifestation of the grand style in which the rulers of the Qi state lived. Used to pour water for ablutions, this vessel was associated with a basin to catch the runoff, but so far its companion basin has not been found. An inscription of 22 graphs cast on the bottom of the vessel records the fact that the Marquis of Qi had it made for Guo Mengji Liangnu who was his wife, called Liangnu and was originally from the state of Guo.

In ancient China, women did not have formal given names. In addition to calling them by their sobriquet,[2] one had to use the name of their state of origin. Qi is a Jiang surname and Guo a Ji one.[3] Thus, this was a marriage uniting two princely families of different surnames. Such marriages also constituted special links between two states and were consequently always charged with a certain amount of political significance.

(1)  齐侯匜.
(2)  An informal given name.
(3)  Jiang 姜 and Ji 姬 refer to very ancient family names and ultimately to place names, more specifically the names of two rivers.

### 40.  *Hu* with Birds, Animals and Dragons, Bronze
*Late Chunqiu period (second half of 6th century–476 B.C.)*
*H: 44.3 cm; D (mouth): 16.6 cm; D (base): 19.0 cm*

A very large group of bronze vessels was excavated in 1923 at Liyu village Hunyuan County in Shanxi Province, including a number of new shapes, of which the most outstanding were a *xi zun* vessel[1] and a pair of *hu* vessels, superbly decorated with birds, animals and dragons. The neck of this *hu* displays three registers of bird-beaked human heads, mythological creatures with animal bodies and bird tails and intertwining dragons. In the last register, some sort of monsters' heads devour coiling dragons. Between the registers, there are rhinoceroses, oxen, tigers, leopards and other small realistic animals, all shown in lively attitudes. Below the belly of the *hu* is a band of wild geese which stand still, their heads raised and their necks crooked, as real as life.

During the Chunqiu period, Hunyuan was located on the border of the Northern Yan and Loufan states, with the Jin state for a neighbor in the south. The shapes and decoration of the vessels of Hunyuan have features peculiar to both Yan and Jin vessels. At that time, this region was under the political control of the Yan state, but, in decorative approach was marked by Yan characteristics with Jin influences. Thus, it could be said that the Hunyuan group is a cross between Jin and Yan vessels. However, this particular vessel is a product of the Jin culture, as molds for the casting of the decoration on such *hu* vessels have been found at the site of the Chunqiu period foundry of Houma city.[2]

(1) *Bronze Vessels in the Collection of the Shanghai Museum* (see Plate 34, footnote (1)), Plate 72.
(2) Archaeological Excavation Committee, Houma City, " 侯馬牛村古城南東周遺址發掘簡報 " ("Houma Niucun gucheng nan Dong Zhou yizhi fajue jianbao", "Brief Report of the Excavations at the Eastern Zhou Site South of the Old City at Niucun, Houma"), *Kaogu*, 1962, no. 2, Plates 1–5.

### 41. *Hu*, Bronze
*Late Chunqiu period (second half of 6th century–476 B.C.)*
*H: 47.5 cm; D (mouth): 15.0 cm; D (bottom): 17.3 cm*

This *hu* is one of a pair. Four upright rings in the shape of animals surmount the lid, two flattened animal mask handles with rings decorate the shoulders and four tiers of feather pattern surround the body. The bottom tier merges into down-pointing lotus petals.

The feather pattern is a modification of animal shapes. Instead of showing entire bodies of animals, it utilizes the small feathers on the bodies of the flying dragons and snakes to form a close-knit design. This type of variation based on a characteristic part of certain animals was in vogue during the late Chunqiu and early Warring States periods. This sort of design is extremely fine and intricate, but since the ceramic mold was made by the repetitious use of the same stamp, the actual making of the vessel would not be too time-consuming. The mold was technically of a relatively high caliber, and the decor is often so minute as to be barely discernible. This is a feature of the bronze casting technique during the Chunqiu and Warring States periods.

### 42. *Ding* with Coiled Dragon Motif, Bronze
*Warring States period (475–221 B.C.)*
*H: 55.0 cm; D (mouth): 57.8 cm*

This *ding* of gigantic proportions has bent ears and cabriole legs. Its lid is surmounted by three rings. Besides the meander pattern forming a large whorl circle[1] on its top, this lid and the vessel itself are each decorated with five bands of interlaced dragons, whose ribbon-like bodies are filled with geometric design. Stylistically such animal patterns belong to the Sanjin area,[2] and pottery molds of this type have been excavated from the bronze foundry site at Houma, Shanxi Province. Smaller *ding* have also been unearthed from Warring States tombs at Changzhi in the same province. This type of coiled dragon motif was in vogue from the end of Chunqiu to the early Warring States period.

(1) In describing this pattern, the Chinese use the graph 囧, which means bright light.
(2) The three states of Wei, Zhao and Han in north central China.

### 43. *Dui* Inlaid with Geometric Designs, Bronze
*Warring States period (475–221 B.C.)*
*H: 25.6 cm; D (body): 18.6 cm*

An innovation of the late Chunqiu period, the *dui* is a food vessel used as a grain container. It looks like a sphere with symmetrical top and bottom which can be used separately and have the same capacity. In this case, the alternation of flat inlaid triangular cloud motifs with ones in raised lines produces a marvelously complex and unusual effect. The upper half of the lid and the lower half of the bottom share the same continuous design of rectangular cloud patterns. Here the background inlaid decoration consists of large areas of coiled fine copper wires alternating with small fragments of glued jade and presents an interesting comparison with the triangular motifs. The apex and bottom are inlaid with whorl circles, and narrow strips of diagonal cloud motifs separate the main zones. The coiled copper wire inlays are for the most part intact, but the glued inlaid

jade fragments have all dropped off. However, the adhesive substance remaining on the vessel retains impressions of the pieces of jade that were once there. This unusually fine and time-consuming piece of art exemplifies the new heights reached in bronze casting at that time.

### 44. Mirror with Four Tigers, Bronze
*Warring States period (475–221 B.C.)*
*D: 12.2 cm*

This mirror is reported to have been unearthed in 1948 from Jincun, Loyang, Henan Province. Its back is divided into four equal parts, each with a tiger in low relief. The heads of the animals face the center, each biting the central knob. The necks are depicted with hair, while meander patterns ornament the bodies. The mirror is thick and heavy, unlike the usually thin mirrors of the Warring States period. The ornamental scheme is very similar to the pottery molds for casting bronze vessels that were unearthed from Houma in Shanxi.[1] The date of this mirror cannot be later than early Warring States.

China has a long history of mirror casting. The earliest mirror was excavated from a late Neolithic Machang type site in Gansu Province, dated to 2300 B.C. A number of them also came from sites belonging to the Qijia culture (2100 B.C.). One example was found in the large Tomb No. 1005 at Houjiazhuang, Anyang, and four more were unearthed from the tomb of Fuhao at the same site in 1976. It is in the late Warring States period that mirrors gained tremendous popularity and became objects of daily use for the common people. The thinly cast Warring States mirrors that have survived in large numbers are all cast in the middle and latter part of the period. This mirror is earlier and is a specimen of the Sanjin area.[2]

(1) 張頷 , Zhang Han, " 侯馬東周遺址鑄銅陶范花紋所見 " ("Houma Dong Zhou yizhi zhutong taofan huawen soujian", "Decorative Motifs Seen on the Pottery Molds for Bronze Casting from the Eastern Zhou Site at Houma"), *Wenwu*, 1961, no. 10.
(2) Cf. Catalogue no. 42, footnote (2).

### 45. *Jarlet* with Handle and Nipple Feet, Impressed Pottery
*Warring States period (475–221 B.C.)*
*H: 11.6 cm; D (mouth): 8.0 cm*

This jarlet was excavated in 1964 from a Warring States tomb at the Qijiadun site in Jinshan County in Shanghai Municipality.

It has a small mouth, a drum-like, compact body, a flat base and rests on three nipple feet. A handle that looks like a broad S-shaped belt runs from the shoulder to the belly. The top of the handle is decorated with applied spirals and the lower part with two groups of incised crosshatching lines. A fine impressed checker design covers the overall body. This fine example of late impressed pottery has a hard and firm clay texture and a pleasing shape.

### 46. *Ding* with a Dragon's Head, Celadon Glazed Stoneware
*Warring States period (475–221 B.C.)*
*H: 14.9 cm; D (mouth): 13.8 cm*

The distinctive features of the Warring States protoporcelains[1] are a relatively thin layer of glaze applied more evenly than during the Chunqiu period and clearly visible wheel marks. The kiln sites so far discovered in Zhejiang Province are those of Fusheng in Shaoxing County and Jinhuaqu in Xiaoshan County.

One side of the mouth of this *ding* is adorned with a dragon head with protruding eyes and a flaming crown across its forehead. A small beast appears below the mouth rim on the opposite side. The two lateral sides carry rectangular, vertical handles, while the three feet resemble animal hooves. The belly has two parallel grooves, and the space between them is incised with parallel slanting lines. The lower part is ornamented with a meander[2] design. The greenish-brown glaze is thin and not too even. It has gathered in spots.

This *ding* belongs to the same category with the proto-porcelain *ding* unearthed at the Huangpu Commune of Shaoxing County in 1974[3] and the pottery *ding* excavated from the cliff tomb of Guixi in Jiangxi Province,[4] which shows that this was a fairly common ceramic shape during the Chunqiu and Warring States periods.

(1) Frequently referred to in English terminology as "Old Yue."
(2) See Catalogue no. 16, footnote (1).
(3) *Kaogu*, 1979, no. 5.
(4) *Wenwu*, 1980, no. 11.

### 47. *Huang* Dragon-headed Pendant with Grain Pattern, Jade
*Warring States period (475–221 B.C.)*
*L: 8.25 cm; W: 2.5 cm*

During the Warring States period, *peiyu*[1] worn as pendants by nobility were extremely ornate. In the entry for *peiyu* in the *Tiangu* chapter, *Yufu* section of the *Zhouli*,[2] Zhengzhu, quoting the *Shizhuan*,[3] says: "The *peiyu* consists of an azure horizontal top-piece and of a double *huang* below. Pearls are strung between them." This piece must have been part of a *peiyu*. Carved in openwork, it is formed of two connecting *huang,* one on top of the other. The top one is an arch-shaped slab, while the bottom part is a double-headed dragon. The entire piece is covered with a grain pattern. The workmanship is exquisite and the shape particularly imaginative. It amply demonstrates the relatively high level of excellence reached in jade carving during the Warring States period.

(1) An elaborate arrangement of various jade pieces, beads and tassels worn as a pendant by the ancient Chinese.
(2) See Catalogue no. 9, footnote (1).
(3) 诗传.

### 48. Fish-shaped *Hu*, Bronze (Colorplate XV)
*Western Han period (206 B.C.–8 A.D.)*
*H: 31.8 cm; D (mouth): 4.4 cm; Base: 12.1 ×20.0 cm*

The whole vessel is a fish. The neck is shaped like a fish head, the foot like a fish tail, and the belly is covered with scales. The vessel is soft and plump and is the result of a natural merging of the characteristics of the fish with the shape of a flattened *hu*.[1] A common motif of the Han dynasty, the fish symbolized love and abundant posterity and was an especially popular motif of decoration for wine and water vessels. This design where a fish is utilized to make up a complete vessel is particularly imaginative.

(1) Refers to a commonly seen bronze vessel shape made during the Warring States period.

### 49. *Bi* Disc with *Kui* Dragons and Animal Masks, Jade
*Han dynasty (206 B.C.–220 A.D.)*
*D: 23.2 cm; Thickness: 0.5 cm*

This *bi*[1] disc, carved from green jade, has the same design on both sides. A rope pattern separates two concentric zones. Finely carved round spirals, arranged in an orderly manner, fill the inner zone. In the outer zone are two symmetrical groups of animal masks and *kui*[2] dragons. The masks look fierce, the tops of the heads bifurcate and open up in snake-like extensions. On either side, these extensions merge into *kui* dragons to form an integrated pattern.

This precious relic of the Han dynasty is carved with accuracy. Its texture is lustrous and the carving technique, with incisions that flow naturally, skillful.

(1) Cf. Catalogue no. 9 where *bi* are mentioned in conjunction with *cong.*
(2) Small, open-mouthed dragons seen in profile. Traditionally the *kui* is said to be a one-legged monster.

### 50. Dish with Cloud Motifs, Lacquer (Colorplate XVII)
*Western Han period (206 B.C.–8 A.D.)*
*H: 3.5 cm; D: 22.5 cm*

Lacquer dishes were used in large quantity as food containers in ancient China. They were particularly popular during the Western Han period as parts of complete sets of eating vessels. The dish was made from a wooden core coated with lacquer. The center of the piece is painted in vermilion with swirling clouds and wedge-shaped motifs against a purplish brown background. A wave pattern runs along the edge, and the inside wall bears three bowstrings with the "IB" motifs that were in great vogue in Western Han lacquers. Said to have been excavated from a Han tomb in Changsha,[1] this dish is finely made and elegantly ornamented.

(1) In Hunan Province.

### 51. "Magic" Mirror, Bronze (Colorplate XIV)
*Western Han period (206 B.C.–8 A.D.)*
*D: 12.1 cm; Thickness: 1.57–1.6 cm; Thinnest point: 1.0 cm*

This mirror "lets the light through," thus, it is popularly called a "transparent mirror." The bulging knob is surrounded by concentric round and overlapping bow-shaped motifs. The outer band is incised with a 20-character inscription which reads as follows: "(Its) inner clarity reflects the light. Like that of the sun and the moon its brilliance does not dissipate." The character " 而 " appears at intervals in this inscription.[1]

This is an object from the mid Western Han period. The face of the mirror is smooth and shiny and can still reflect images, but in sunlight or in a direct light beam it can also reflect a shadow image corresponding to its back, hence the term "transparent." Since the Sui and Tang dynasties, many books have recorded the phenomenon presented by these mirrors, and many conjectures have been made as to the way they were cast. The theory is that the mirror face has tiny ripples which cannot be seen by the naked eye but which magnify the optical path of the passing light, thus, creating an uneven ratio in the diffusion of the reflecting light and causing the light penetration phenomenon by forming bright shadows of various intensities. As to the cause of the mirror's rippling surface, experimentation revealed that during the casting process the rate of cooling was not the same, depending upon the thickness of the various parts of the mirror, which caused deformations due to stress. When the shiny surface was being polished, this could also produce additional pressure stress. It is the accumulation of these stress factors which brought about structural changes in the metal and produced on the surface of the mirror the minute wrinkles which correspond to the decor on the back of the mirror.

(1) The exact meaning of the character in this particular context is still under study.

### 52. Mirror with Various Supernatural Beings, Bronze
*Eastern Han period, dated 187 A.D.*
*D: 19.0 cm*

Three *bixie* and a *feilian*[1] guard the main axes of this mirror, and the intervals are filled with supernatural human beings, including attendants, feathered men, as well as with other supernatural animals. The outer rim displays two groups of figures. One group consists of a chariot pulled by six dragons. An immortal and a feathered being sit erect in the chariot while a supernatural being manages the dragons in front of the chariot. The second group consists of a feathered being riding on the azure bird[2] and a supernatural being riding on the tortoise. Between the two groups a being holds the solar disc, next to him is the golden bird[3] and across from it is the toad. In Chinese mythology the bird and toad represent the sun and moon, respectively.

Broken up in small square sections, an inscription where all of the 52 characters are reversed reads:

"On the *wu* day of the fifth month of the fourth year of the Zhongping reign, secretly refining white brass, I made a lustrous mirror. The buyer (of it) will have great wealth and will forever have sons and grandsons. With extended years, his destiny will be long-lasting, such as that of the Royal Father[4] and the Royal Mother of the West,[5] represented here. His great happiness will be without end and his long life will be full of good luck (like) the days and months of the King of Heaven and the long destiny of the Great Tutor."[6]

The fourth year of Zhongping is equivalent to 187 A.D. This mirror belongs to the period of Han Lingdi Liu Hong.[7] Superbly cast, it exemplifies the very high standard achieved in mirror casting of that period.

(1)  *Bixie* ( 辟邪 ), see Catalogue no. 57, footnote (1). Feilian ( 飞廉 ), a mythical animal and god of the wind. According to a 2nd century source, it has the body of a deer, the head of a small bird, horns and a snake tail and marks of a leopard.
(2)  Feathered men are humans who become immortals. The azure bird is one of three birds attached to Xiwangmu, the Queen Mother of the West. See footnote (6) below.
(3)  The golden bird, another one of the three birds attached to Xiwangmu. See footnote (2) above and (6) below.
(4) and (5)  The Queen Mother of the West, Xiwangmu, lives in the Kunlun Mountain (in present-day Sichuan) and possesses the secret of the elixir of immortality. The Royal Father (of the East) is her geographic counterpart, a much later development in Chinese religion and seemingly of no great importance except as a balance to Xiwangmu.
(6)  Taishi ( 太师 ). an official rank in the Zhou dynasty, transplanted here into the celestial bureaucracy that was developed during the Han dynasty.
(7)  An emperor who reigned from 168 to 188 A.D.

### 53.  Dog, Brown-glazed Pottery
*Han dynasty (206 B.C.–220 A.D.)*
*H: 48.5 cm; L: 46.8 cm*

The repertory of low-fired, lead-glazed *mingqi*[1] models made during the Han dynasty is quite extensive, and the sculptural quality of such models is of a very high caliber.

The dog is a common subject among animal figurines. This brown-glazed, crouching dog raises its head and barks away. Looking like a lively braggart, this figurine was not intended to reflect any particular situation or outward appearance but to emphasize the inner life of the animal. The treatment is direct and concise. This is an excellent specimen for studying the union of decoration and expression in ancient traditional sculpture.

(1)  Articles to be buried with the dead. See Plate 65.

### 54.  Duck, Green-glazed Pottery (Colorplate XVIII)
*Han dynasty (206 B.C.–220 A.D.)*
*H: 21.7 cm; L: 26.0 cm*

Brown and green are the colors most commonly encountered in the low-fired, lead glazes of the Han dynasty. The coloring agent for the green glaze is copper. When remaining in a damp environment and being exposed over a long period of time to the corroding and sedimentary action of water and air, the glaze develops at certain points of contact an extremely fine layer of sediments. After the process has been repeated over and over again and after the glaze has reached a certain thickness, its slightly emulsive quality and the light rays produce a white luster known as "silver glaze." The silver glaze of this duck is the result of such circumstances.

This piece exemplifies a fairly high artistic level; the posture and characteristics of the duck are clearly stated: it is gentle and lovely, and the modeling is concise and skillful.

### 55.  Jar with Architectural Elements and Human Figurines, Celadon Stoneware (Colorplate XVI)
*Western Jin period (265–316 A.D.)*
*H (overall): 49.7 cm*

Jars carrying the model of a storied watchtower and human figurines are commonly found in tombs from the Wu[1] and Western Jin[2] periods. These jars were *mingqi*[3] where food was stored for the "tomb master" (the deceased). They developed out of the "five-jar clusters"[4] of the Eastern Han.[5] Their shape and decoration are quite involved. The jars serve as the main body, and their mouths are piled up with human figurines, birds, animals and a storied watchtower creating busy scenes full of liveliness. Various types of human, avian and animal effigies are applied on the belly of the piece, and some jars also bear various *nien-hao*,[6] such as Yongan[7] and Yuankang,[8] as well as auspicious inscriptions.

A row of applied warriors surrounds the upper part of this particular jar, which has a rotund belly. The watchtower on the mouth has three stories: the lowest story consists of the gate and its keepers, the second story is a house with corner pavilions and the third story, which is also the lid of the vessel, is the roof. The celadon glaze stops short of the foot.

(1)  Wu (222–280 A.D.)
(2)  Western Jin (265–316 A.D.)
(3)  Cf. Catalogue no. 53, footnote (1).
(4)  So far found only south of the Yangzi, these consist of five small or miniature jars connected side to side.
(5)  Eastern Han (25–220 A.D.)
(6)  Title(s) of an emperor's reign.
(7)  Yongan ( 永安 ) (258–264 A.D.)
(8)  Yuankang ( 元康 ) (291–299 A.D.)

### 56.  Frog-shaped Water Container, Celadon Stoneware
*Western Jin period (265–316 A.D.)*
*H: 3.85 cm; L: 7.8 cm; D (mouth): 3.5 cm*

During the Western Jin period, celadon stoneware production reached a new height, not only in terms of quantity, but also in terms of complexity in shapes, of variety in decorative skills and of the pleasing lustrous effect of glazes.

This water container is one of the most exquisite works of its kind. This frog-shaped container has a tight mouth, a flattened body and a round, solid foot. The frog's legs are applied, and its back has a circular opening. The body is decorated with circles and dotted lines and is entirely covered with a shiny and lustrous celadon glaze.

This lively object is similar to another frog-shaped water container excavated in 1973 by the Tongjing Commune in Jiangning County, Jiangsu Province.[1]

(1)  See *Wenwu*, 1975, no. 2.

## 57. Ram, Celadon Stoneware
*Eastern Jin period (317–419 A.D.)*
*H:14.3 cm; L:15.8 cm*

By the time of the Three Kingdoms and Eastern and Western Jin, the techniques for firing celadon stonewares were fully developed, and the variety of artifacts and of their shapes had increased considerably. Animal-shaped containers, such as rams and *bixie*,[1] were relatively common.

The glaze of this ram is a bluish green. His four legs are tucked beneath his body in a recumbent attitude. His tail looks like a banana leaf, and his two horns curl around his ears, forming a forward-moving curve. A small round hole on top of his head gives access to the body, and a pair of wings is incised on his flanks. With its shiny green glaze, this compelling portrait is basically similar to another ram unearthed from Tomb No. 7 on Mt. Xiang in Nanjing.[2] It is indeed a very fine piece.

> (1) Originally designating a fabulous animal resembling a long-tailed deer with two horns, the term has for some time been loosely applied to winged and horned felines of the lion or tiger class. Literally the term *bixie* means "to ward off evil influences."
> (2) See *Wenwu*, 1972, no. 11.

## 58. Bodhisattva Padmapani, Gilt Bronze
*Made by Baoliang*
*Northern Wei period (501 A.D.)*
*H:15.0 cm*

The bodhisattva wears a crown over his high chignon. His face is emaciated, and his right hand carries a lotus bud. His torso is bare, but he wears a fluttering scarf. The lotus-petal-shaped nimbus is decorated with low relief flames and a lotus flower. The back of the nimbus is engraved with the Buddhas Shakyamuni and Prabhūtaratna. The incised decoration of the dais shows two donors on the front and floral scroll work on the sides. The 14-character inscription engraved on the dais reads:

> "Made by Bhiksu Baoliang on the 22nd day of the fifth month in the second year of Jingming."

The second year of Jingming is the first reign title of Emperor Xuanwu of Northern Wei and corresponds to 501 A.D.

This bodhisattva is typical of the Northern Wei style.

## 59. Standing Buddha, Bronze
*Northern Wei period (386–534 A.D.)*
*H: 35.5 cm*

The hair of this Buddha is wavy. He sports a faint smile and his hands make the reassurance and gift-bestowing gestures. His monastic robe, baring his right shoulder, has fine striated folds and has not fully departed from the Indian Buddhist sculptural tradition. The nimbus is rather ornate; its outer zone consisting of thick flames in low relief, while fine flames are incised on the tip of the lotus petals in the middle zone and five concentric bands, two of them beaded, decorate the inner zone.

The engraving is forceful and sharp. It reveals the work of the cutting tool in all its keenness. This sculpture somewhat differs from the emaciated style of Northern Wei and may point to the later part of that period.

## 60. Buddhist Shrine, Gilt bronze (Colorplate XIX)
*Sui dynasty (589–618 A.D.)*
*H: 37.6 cm; L: (at base): 23.4 cm; W (at base): 30.4 cm*

The hair of the central Buddha is wavy. His right shoulder is bare, and he makes the preaching gesture, while sitting cross-legged on the lotus throne. An unusual row of human faces surrounds the constricted waist of the lotus pedestal. Flames in openwork decorate the outer border of the halo, while the inside, also in openwork, is made of floral scrolls and miniature images of the Seven Buddhas of the Past. The two openings in the pedestal on either side of the central image were meant for the insertion of two attendant figures, now lost.

The two attendant bodhisattvas, bedecked with pearl tassels, wear high chignons and crowns; their upper torsos are bare and scarves flutter from their shoulders down. One holds a precious pearl and the other precious flowers.

Flanking them are two donor figures. The lady donor wears a robe with narrow sleeves and a silk scarf and holds an object in her hand. The male donor holds his hands in the gesture of adoration. In the foreground are two lions, Guardians of the Law, with large mouths and lolling tongues.

This group of Buddhist statuettes has elegant, well-rounded bodies and conveys a sense of pure beauty. It is an outstanding sculpture of the Sui dynasty.

## 61. Seated Buddha, Gilt bronze
*Tang dynasty (618–907 A.D.)*
*H:18.0 cm*

Sitting erect with a smooth unadorned coiffure, the Buddha looks very lifelike. The folds of his monastic robes, which leave his right shoulder bare, fall naturally and give a silky appearance to the garment. He holds up his right hand to make the gesture of the Turning of the Wheel of the Law, and his left hand is slightly raised in a preaching gesture. He is seated cross-legged on a Sumeru throne. The result of mature casting, his posture is excellent. It successfully conveys a sense of serenity and intimacy. It is obviously a work of the High Tang period.

## 62. Guanyin, Gilt bronze
*Tang dynasty (618–907 A.D.)*
*H: 29.7 cm*

The bodhisattva with jeweled crown, full, rounded face, elongated eyes and brows, bare chest, brooches and necklaces covering his body, armlets and bracelets, and the scarf that coils around his arms must be Guanyin. The gestures of his hands indicate that they once held the flask for holy water and willow branch, attributes that are now lost. This piece still retains some Indian Buddhist features, especially in the bare torso bedecked with jewels. Guanyin is a male figure, but there is something feminine in the beautiful structure of this body. Tang bodhisattvas are effeminate, just like some ancient Greek and Roman sculptures. The lower half of this sculpture is relatively short, a feature shared by many sculptures of the Tang dynasty.

## 63. Openwork Phoenix Plaque, Jade (Colorplate XX)
*Tang dynasty (618–907 A.D.)*
*L:16.2 cm; W: 7.8 cm*

The oblong jade ornament displays an openwork design of a pair of phoenixes among convoluting clouds. The bodies of the birds are covered with finely incised feathers. Shown in profile, they face each other. Their fluttering tails and wide open beaks suggest that they are singing and dancing. They create a lively image of elegant seduction. The carving, design and technique of this rare and precious piece that was handed down by successive generations are very close in style to the silver gold vessels of the Tang dynasty.

## 64. Mallow-shaped Mirror, Bronze
*Tang dynasty (618–907 A.D.)*
*D: 24.7 cm*

This mallow-shaped mirror is decorated with conventionalized flowers of various shapes. Tang dynasty design is heavily influenced by Buddhist art, and this type of motif is made of a real flower combined with one imagined by the craftsman. It is a type of *baoxianghua*[1] or a derivation of it, but it is superbly designed. When compared to the mythical motifs of Han mirrors,[2] this one conveys a feeling of freshness and elegance.

(1) 宝相花 an idealized flower used in Buddhist art, which combines the best parts of chrysanthemum, lotus and peony, etc.
(2) See Figure 52.

## 65. Tray with Three Feet and Decoration of Flying Birds and Cloud Scrolls, Polychrome Glazed Pottery
*Tang dynasty (618–907 A.D.)*
*H: 6.4 cm; D (mouth): 31.6 cm*

The general appellation "Tang period polychrome glazed pottery" refers to lead-glazed pottery of such colors as yellow, green, white, blue and reddish brown. Commonly known as "Tang three-color pottery," this ware was very popular. It was fashionable at home and was also exported to such places as Southeast Asia and Africa. In addition, it was successfully imitated in Japan, Korea and other countries.

There are numerous kinds of three-color pottery objects. Besides human and animal figurines, there are utensils for daily use, such as trays, bowls, vases, jars, toys, etc. However, ultimately all kinds were used as *mingqi*, i.e., articles to be buried with the dead.

The decoration of this tray is divided into three concentric rings, separated from one another by grooves. The outer ring is decorated with six clouds, the middle one with six flying geese and the central one with a geometric floral motif. The glazes are yellow, green, blue and white. Three rope-like, circular feet are attached to the base.

So far one kiln that produced this kind of polychrome glazed pottery has been discovered. It is the Huangye kiln in Gong County, Henan Province.

## 66. Female Rider, Polychrome Glazed Pottery
(Colorplate XXII)
*Tang dynasty (618–907 A.D.)*
*H: 39.2 cm; L: 38.7 cm*

Horses played a prominent role in Tang social life, and horseback riding was much in vogue at all levels of Tang society. This is reflected in poetry, polychrome glazed pottery figurines and paintings, such as Zhang Xuan's "Lady Guoguo's Spring Outing" and the mural paintings in the tomb of Prince Zhang Huai (Li Xian).

This female rider wears a hood and a long close-fitting gown with a low neck and tight sleeves. The horse is covered with a white glaze; the tail, hooves and saddlecloth, as well as the lady's garment, are covered separately with brown, green and white glazes, whereas the saddle, the lady's hood and her facial features are painted with black pigments. The lady, her manner relaxed, looks straight ahead with both hands positioned to hold the reins. The horse is big, strong and well proportioned, a most successful piece of sculpture.

## 67. Female Rider in Foreign Attire, Polychrome Glazed Pottery
*Tang dynasty (618–907 A.D.)*
*H: 42.1 cm; L: 34.0 cm*

The Tang practiced a system of elaborate funerals. Not only "do kings, dukes and all officials have lavish funerals," but "the custom is spreading rapidly and is reaching the scholars and the people."[1] Consequently, large quantities of polychrome glazed potteries were placed in tombs with the dead. Figurines on horseback were therefore made especially as *mingqi* to accompany the deceased. They also reflected the pleasures that the deceased had experienced while they were alive.

This female rider with a plump, made-up face wears a red "wind hat"[2] and green foreign clothes.[3] She rides a brown horse with a trimmed mane. Its saddle and saddlecloth, the lady's hat, as well as her face, are all painted in red, black and other pigments.

This figure leans back and looks ahead. She seems to be restraining the horse, which turns its head to the left in response. The posture is wonderfully natural.

(1) 唐会要 (*Tang Huiyao*, vol. 38).
(2) A cowl-like winter hat.
(3) Refers to costumes worn by nomadic peoples during the Warring States and Western Han periods.

## 68. Seated Female Figurine, Polychrome Glazed Pottery
*Tang dynasty (618–907 A.D.)*
*H: 33.8 cm*

Human figurines form the bulk of polychrome glazed pottery. These figurines are not only true to life, well-proportioned, distinctive and skillfully done, they also illustrate different social positions and ranks, as well as individual expressions. The attitudes and attires of female figurines are particularly striking. They all reveal a very high level of technical and artistic ability.

This figurine has her hair done into two high chignons. Her face is painted. Shown in glossy green, white and brown colors that run into one another, her tight-sleeved jacket and pleated skirt are tied around the waist. The skirt is ample and falls to the ground. A green scarf covers her shoulders and loops in front of her partly exposed chest. She also wears trefoiled shoes with white soles. Her left hand rests on her lap, and she holds a flower against her chest with her right one. She is gazing fixedly and looks genial and passive as she sits on a stool that looks like a narrow-waisted drum.

## 69. Female Figurine, Painted and gilded pottery
*Tang dynasty (618–907 A.D.)*
*H: 55.6 cm*

Just like their glazed counterparts, painted pottery figurines unearthed from Tang tombs are lively, beautifully painted and display many different postures and costumes. Some have gilded decoration, which makes them look even more refined and precious. They give a general idea of what daily life was in those days and bringing together sculpture and painting constitute a remarkable artistic accomplishment.

This figurine wears a lopsided, knife-like chignon. Her face is made up with fine eyebrows and graceful eyes. She is dressed in a jacket with narrow sleeves, a scarf over the partly exposed chest, a long, floor-length skirt and round-headed shoes. Her left arm is hanging, and she holds her bent right arm close to her chest as if holding something.

She is painted with red, white and black pigments, as well as with gold color. The pigments have faded and are hardly visible.

## 70. Phoenix-headed Pitcher, Polychrome glazed pottery
*Tang dynasty (618–907 A.D.)*
*H: 31.5 cm*

The development of communications between China and the West during the Tang dynasty brought about an increase in cultural contacts and exchanges with the outside world, as well as an input of many foreign influences. For example, such handsome shapes as this phoenix-headed pitcher in polychrome glazed pottery were created with the inspiration of Persian culture. Objects of this type are frequently unearthed from Tang tombs and have also been found abroad.

This particular vessel has a small mouth, a slender neck, and oval, flattened body, a high foot and a flat base. The region of the mouth and neck is decorated with a phoenix head. On the opposite side is a bow-shaped, tubular handle. Both sides of the body bear impressed designs, one side with a phoenix and the other with a warrior on horseback and hunting with a bow.

This refined object has a brown and green two-color glaze, is well rounded, sleek and elegant. This type of pitcher was made with a two-part mold and such molds have been discovered at the Huangye kiln site in Gong County, Henan Province.

**71. Horse, Pottery with Underglaze White Spots**
*Tang dynasty (618–907 A.D.)*
*H: 66.0 cm; L: 73.0 cm*

Horses and camels are frequently found in Tang sculpture, where they stand as extraordinarily successful works of art. This has to do with the important role which these animals played at that time in trade and cultural exchanges between China and the outside world. The horse, particularly, was an indispensable means of locomotion in warfare and everyday life and, as such, was represented as an outstanding, refined and lively animal.

This horse was not made as Tang three-color pottery is usually done. Spots were first painted on the horse's body with slurry; then the piece was covered with a transparent glaze and fired. The result was an underglaze white, mottled effect. The animal is saddled and stands still. Its lower jaw and four hooves are decorated with a brown glaze and its mouth is open as if it were neighing. Running the length of the back of its neck a deep groove was originally fitted with a mane.

**72. Two-eared Jarlet,**
**Stoneware with Color Blotches on a Black Glaze**
*Tang dynasty (618–907 A.D.)*
*H: 11.3 cm; D (mouth): 7.6 cm; D (base): 7.7 cm*

Stonewares with color blotches on a black glaze are an innovation of the Tang period. They were produced in Lushan, Jia, Neixiang and Yu Counties, Henan Province, as well as in Jiaocheng County in Shanxi Province.

This jar has a curled lip, a short neck, a spherical belly and a solid foot and is equipped with a pair of ears placed symmetrically on its shoulders. The black glaze, which stops short of the foot, contains ashy-blue blotches that run irregularly. The shape is full, the contours round and smooth, and the color spots elegant and pleasant to the eye. This is an accomplished specimen of two-color glazed pottery.

**73. Bowl, Xing Ware Porcelain**
*Tang dynasty (618–907 A.D.)*
*H: 3.4 cm; D (mouth): 15.0 cm; D (foot): 7.0 cm*

The Xing kilns are famous northern kilns of the Tang dynasty. Historical records mention them in the same breath with the southern Yue kilns. Lu Yu, in his *Chajing*,[1] denigrates Xing wares and praises Yue wares, stating: "Xing is not as good as Yue on three counts." However, his is just the viewpoint of a tea sipper. For a long time no one knew what this silver or snow-like Xing porcelain really looked like because the kilns where it was made had not been located. However, in October 1980 Xing kiln sites were discovered in two places—Qicun and Shuangjin in Lincheng County, Hebei Province—and thus solved the puzzle posed by Xing porcelain.

The Xing kilns produced two types of wares: one coarse, the other fine. The coarse type resembles the stonewares produced at other Tang kilns. Paste and glaze are crude and disguised with slip; the glaze is only applied halfway down the outside; inside the wares show three scars made by the three-pronged pads used to pile them on top of one another during firing. Exquisitely produced, the fine type consists of perfect shapes with white paste and pure, soft and lustrous glazes that fit the descriptions given by the annals.

This perfectly circular bowl has a lipped mouth rim, a base shaped like a jade *bi* disc[2] and is glazed all over, except for the ring of the foot.

(1) *Chajing* ( 茶经 ), the *Tea Classic,* was an illustrated treatise on the nature and etiquette of tea drinking.
(2) For a jade *bi* disc, see Figure 49.

**74. Grain Container with Four Handles and Engraved Decoration, Yue Ware**
*Five Dynasties period (907–960 A.D.)*
*H (overall): 24.6 cm; D (mouth): 9.75 cm; D (base): 8.2 cm*

The Yue kilns which centered around Shanglinhu in present-day Yuyao County, Zhejiang Province, were so named because in the old days this region was part of the Yue Prefecture.

This production is based on the celadon glazed stonewares made during the Han, Wu and two Jin periods.[1] During the Tang, Five Dynasties and early part of the Northern Song periods, the production never ceased to improve. Yue stonewares are reputed for the fineness and smoothness of their paste, the luster of their glazes and elegance of their incised decoration.

During the Tang period, the majority of Yue vessels were plain. Only toward the end of the period did rather coarse, incised patterns appear. Then from the Five Dynasties to the Northern Song periods the decoration on Yue wares became elegant and refined. The shapes, too, from sober and ponderous, as they had previously been, tended to become elegant and beautiful.

A grain container, this jar served as a piece of grave furniture, and it is similar to the one in the collection of the Administrative Committee for Cultural Affairs in Shaoxing County, Zhejiang Province, which is dated by inscription to 998 A.D.[2]

(1) Wu (222–280 A.D.), Western Jin (265–316 A.D.), Eastern Jin (317–420 A.D.).
(2) See 浙江省文物考古所学刊 (*Zhejiangsheng Wenwu Kaoguso Xuekan*), 1981.

**75. Comb Top with Floral Motif, Jade**
*Northern Song dynasty (960–1127 A.D.)*
*L: 12.3 cm; W: 4.4 cm*

This thin, lustrous jade comb top with a closely-knit incised design of mallow flowers recalls the style of the gold and silver ornamentation of the Tang and Five Dynasties. Carved with skill and elegance, this piece is regular and beautiful and conveys a feeling of warmth and serenity. To execute such fine details on a thin slab of jade presents great difficulties. The result demonstrates the technical dexterity achieved by the craftsmen of that period.

**76. Bodhisattva, Gilt bronze** (Colorplate XXI)
*Song dynasty (960–1279 A.D.)*
*H: 13.5 cm*

The bodhisattva wears a convoluted crown studded with precious jewels. He is fully clothed, no longer like the Sui and Tang dynasty examples which have quite a bit of their bodies showing. His garments are Chinese, and his jewelry is limited to a necklace. The bodhisattva concept gradually eroded the spiritual aspect of religion and made it more mundane so that worldly people were used as models for

Buddhist sculpture. This is a characteristic of Chinese Buddhist sculpture of the later periods.

### 77. Mahāsthāmaprāpta, Gilt Bronze
*Song dynasty (960–1279 A.D.)*
*H: 33.0 cm*

Wearing an elaborate crown, the round-cheeked, stately bodhisattva carries strings of jewels hanging from his neck and waist. He wears a cassock over his shoulders and a floor-length inner garment that exposes his cloud-patterned right shoe. His right arm, bent and showing the palm of his hand, points to the earth, while the attribute once held in his left hand is now lost. This type of bodhisattva figure, fully clothed and wearing a floor-length inner garment, is typical of the Song style. Mahāsthāmaprāpta is equal in stature to Guanyin. They are both attendants to the Buddha Amitabha with whom they form a triad.

### 78. Porcelain Plate with Molded Design of Dragon and Clouds, Ding Ware
*Northern Song dynasty (960–1127 A.D.)*
*H: 4.5 cm; D (mouth): 23.3 cm; D (foot): 10.8 cm*

Ding ware is one of the five famous Song wares. Located in present-day Jianci and Yanchuan villages in Quyang County, Hebei Province, the kilns produced essentially white porcelains and accessory wares with other colors, such as green, purple and black.

Ding wares have thin bodies, soft glazes and regular shapes. The designs were applied in many different methods, including molding, carving and incising, molding being the most favored method.

In order to meet a great demand, the Ding potters of the Five Dynasties introduced the technique of firing the objects upside down. The disadvantage of this technique was that the mouths of the objects were unglazed and developed hairy edges (also known as "straw mouths").[1] This is why mouthrims are frequently bound with gold, silver and copper rims.

This plate is bound with a copper rim and decorated with a molded design of clouds and dragons. It is said to have been made by court order for imperial use. The extraordinary clarity of the pattern reflects the degree of excellence reached at the time in the technique of carving and applying molds.

(1) 芒口 .

### 79. Celadon Vase on Three Feet with Carved Decoration, Yaozhou Ware (Colorplate XXV)
*Northern Song dynasty (960–1127 A.D.)*
*H: 21.4 cm; D (mouth): 8.0 cm*

The Yaozhou kilns were located in present-day Huangbaozhen in Tongchuan City, Shaanxi Province. They began to be active during the Tang dynasty when they produced many kinds of wares. During the Song dynasty, they developed greatly, but concentrated on celadons. Because these wares were similar to those produced by the southern kilns of Longquan, they used to be known as "Northern Longquan" celadons.[1]

Such techniques of ornamentation as carving and molding were employed at the Yaozhou kilns, but carved pieces are the most refined.

This vase has a curled mouth, a long neck and a round belly resting on three feet with animal masks. The neck and belly are decorated with a continuous pattern of lotus petals and scrolls. In this successful specimen of Yaozhou ware, the carving is forceful, with lively and fluid lines, and there are yellow highlights in the green glaze that covers the whole piece.

(1) In English these are usually referred to as "Northern Celadons."

### 80. Stoneware Basin on Three Feet with Drum Nail Decor, Jun Ware
*Northern Song dynasty (960–1127 A.D.)*
*H: 9.3 cm; D (mouth): 24.0 cm; D (base): 17.7 cm*

With Juntai in Yu County, Henan Province, as its kiln type, Jun ware is one of the five famous Song wares. During the late Northern Song period, Jun kilns became imperial kilns, and the bulk of their output consisted of dishes, trays, goblets and basins. The bases of these objects were often carved with a number from one to ten. Judging from the information collected in recent years during the excavation of the Baguadong kiln site, these numbers were meant to identify vessels of the same category by their size from the largest to the smallest. All the vessels marked "1" were the tallest or those with the largest diameters in their category, while those marked "10" were the shortest or those with the smallest diameters.

The glaze of this basin is essentially very pale blue and sky blue, and the number "1" carved on its base indicates that it belongs to the largest category of three-legged basins. In addition, there are two lines of characters engraved in the center of the base. The horizontal one reads: "Ying Tai."[1] The other, vertical, reads: "(To be) used in Cheng Huai Studio."[2] During the Qing dynasty, this basin was a palace piece, and the inscriptions were carved at that time by the jade section of the imperial workshop.

(1) 瀛台: the "Ocean Platform," referring to a platform symbolizing the Southern Seas and located in the middle of the Tai Ye Pond in the western precincts of the Forbidden City.
(2) 澄怀堂用 : "(To be) used in the Studio of Pure Intentions," which was a hall within the Qing imperial palace compound.

### 81. Porcellaneous Dish, Ru Ware (Colorplate XXIII)
*Northern Song dynasty (960–1127 A.D.)*
*H: 3.4 cm; D (mouth): 13.5 cm; D (foot): 9.0 cm*

Ru ware is one of the five famous Song wares. Tradition has it that Ru kilns were located in the region of present-day Linru County, Henan Province, but there is still no way to determine exactly where this production took place.

The Song writer Ye Zhi has recorded in the *Tan Zhai Bi Heng*:[1] "The present Imperial Court considering that the Dingzhou white porcelains are not fit for use because of their 'straw mouths'[2] ordered Ruzhou to produce azure wares." This shows that the Ru kilns started to produce after the Ding kilns had offered their porcelain to the court and that they worked exclusively for the palace.

The Ru potters corrected the "straw mouth" defect caused by the practice followed at the Ding kilns of firing their wares upside down. As a rule, they used minute nail-shaped spurs during firing, which allowed their wares to be completely glazed inside as well as outside and left only three to five extremely small "nail scars" on the bases of the wares.

This dish, covered with a "sky blue" glaze, is finely crazed all over and has three "nail scars" on its foot the size of sesame seeds. It has passed through the generations for a typical Ru ware.

(1) 坦斋笔衡 , a 13th century publication.
(2) See Catalogue no. 78, footnote (1).

### 82. Porcellaneous Vase with Pierced Ears, Ge Ware
*Southern Song dynasty (1127–1279 A.D.)*
*H: 10.1 cm; D (mouth): 2.3 cm; D (foot): 4.2 cm*

According to tradition, Ge ware is one of the five famous Song wares. Since all extant Ge wares have been handed down from one generation to another, there is no way to determine where they were made, and since in addition no Song tomb has yet yielded an example of the ware, much work remains to be done with regard to the extant pieces.

Well-controlled products, these have thick bodies and shiny glazes. Glaze colors are principally greyish green, light green or hulled rice yellow, and bodies are covered with wide and narrow crackles. The wide crackles assume a deep brown color, and the narrow ones a hulled rice yellow color. The crackles form a crisscross pattern and used to be known as "Gold Threads and Iron Wires."

This precious vase imitates the shape of a bronze *Touhu*.[1] Its glaze is greenish grey, and the crackle covers the entire object.

    (1)  投壶. Refers to the game of pitchpot, in which arrows kept in the ears of the vessel are pitched from a distance into the mouth of the pot.

### 83. Vase, Porcellaneous Guan Ware
*Southern Song dynasty (1127–1279 A.D.)*
*H: 13.9 cm; D (mouth): 2.6 cm; D (foot): 4.7 cm*

Guan ware is one of the five famous Song wares. The Song writer Gu Wenjian writes in his *Fu Xuan Za Lu:*[1] "During the Zhengde and Xuanhe periods,[2] the capital established its own kiln and named it Guan."[3] However, it is still not possible to distinguish which of the surviving Guan wares that have been handed down from one generation to another are Northern Song wares. After the passage of the Song imperial household to the South, it established at Linan (present-day Hangzhou in Zhejiang Province) two kilns—the Xiuneisi[4] and the Jiaotanxia[5]—referred to collectively as the Southern Song Guan kilns. As of today, the only wares that can be identified with certainty are those of the Jiaotanxia kiln.

With Guan wares: "The pure clay used for the body is supremely refined." The wares are decorated with crackles obtained by utilizing the difference in expansion coefficients between body and glaze. Also because of a fairly high iron content in the paste, on mouth rims where the glaze is relatively thin and on feet which it does not cover, appear what is known as "purple mouth and iron feet."

A good example of Guan ware, this vase has the shape of a hanging "gall bladder" and a greenish-grey glaze with "iron wire" crackle.

    (1)  负喧杂录, a late 13th century publication.
    (2)  1111–1125 A.D.
    (3)  Also known as "official kiln."
    (4)  修内司: Bureau of Repairs of Imperial Palace and Ancestral Temple.
    (5)  郊坛下: Below the Sacrificial Altar to Heaven and Earth located on the outskirts of the Southern Song imperial city.

### 84. Celadon *Cong*-shaped Vase, Longquan Ware
(Colorplate XXVI)
*Southern Song dynasty (1127–1279 A.D.)*
*H: 28.6 cm; D (mouth): 8.7 cm; Length of sides:*
*11.6 cm; D (foot): 10.2 cm*

The celadon wares of the Longquan kilns in Longquan County, Zhejiang Province, developed on the traditions laid down by the Ou and Yue kilns and reached their period of splendor during the Southern Song and Yuan dynasties.

The Southern Song Longquan wares won the battle where glaze colors are concerned. The method of repetitive applications of glaze was adopted by the potters working in these kilns causing the glaze layers to assume a natural, moistened effect. Powdery green and plum green are their most successful shades. The glaze of this vase is powdery green with the lustre of jade, and the shape of the vessel imitates that of an ancient jade *cong*.[1]

    (1)  See Colorplate I.

### 85. Bowl, Lacquer
*Southern Song dynasty (1127–1279 A.D.)*
*H: 9.0 cm; D: 16.0 cm*

With its withdrawn mouth rim, curved profile, flat bottom, well-trimmed contours and comparatively thin walls, this vessel is made of plain black lacquer applied to a circular bowl. Plain but beautiful, this type of glossy black lacquer vessel is also durable. It was widely in use in the Song dynasty. This vessel was unearthed in 1972 from the Southern Song Tan family tomb in the Yuepu Commune, Baoshan County, Shanghai Municipality, together with ten other lacquer basins and boxes.

Lacquer manufacture was highly developed in the Song dynasty. Many lacquer pieces have been excavated from Song dynasty tombs in Huian, Heqiao of Yixing and Wuxi in Jiangsu Province, as well as in Wuhan and Fuzhou. Most of these pieces consist of a bamboo or wooden core coated with glossy black or brownish red lacquer, with a lustre that looks brand new. Some have inscriptions painted in lacquer that give the date and place of production and name of the craftsmen who made them. Inscribed place names such as Hangzhou, Wenzhou, Jiangningfu and Xiangzhou clearly indicate that the provinces of Jiangsu, Chejiang and Hubei were important lacquer centers in the Song dynasty.

### 86. Stoneware Bowl with Sky Blue Glaze and Red Suffusions, Jun Ware (Colorplate XXIV)
*Jin Dynasty (1115–1234 A.D.)*
*H: 8.9 cm; D (mouth): 15.0 cm; D (foot): 4.9 cm*

Jun kilns are famous for their successful firings of copper red glazes, of which "crab apple red" and "rose purple" are the ultimate. They also produced a great quantity of wares with blue glazes and red suffusions, the like of which is not to be found in any other contemporaneous wares. These copper red splashes blend into an expanse of sky blue glaze and produce a remarkable effect, evoking the rosy clouds that appear in the western sky at sunset.

Belonging to the type known as "chicken-heart bowls," this particular piece has a withdrawn mouth, a small foot and a deep depression at the center of the base. It is ornamented on the outside with three splashes of varying shades of red, which look like rouge. The inside of the ring foot is glazed.

### 87. Stoneware "Wang Family" Pillow Decorated with Characters in a Scene, Cizhou Ware (Colorplate XXVIII)
*Jin dynasty (1115–1234 A.D.)*
*H: 13.7 cm; W: 17.4 cm; L: 29.8 cm*

The Cizhou kilns were located in the region of present-day Pengcheng and Guantai in Hebei Province. They flourished during the Northern Song, Jin and Yuan dynasties when they produced many kinds of objects, the bulk of which have designs painted in black against a white ground.

This type of painted ware was made by dressing the unfired body with a slip, painting the decor with a brush, applying a transparent glaze and then firing the object. At that time, a wide area over present-day Hebei, Henan and Shanxi produced this kind of stoneware with black decoration on a white ground and formed a network of Cizhou kilns.

A scene with characters from the story "Burning Incense to Worship the Moon"[1] is painted on the top of this pillow. Symmetrical floral paintings decorate the four sides.

The inscription "Made by the Wang Family" was impressed on the base with a seal. In shape and style, this pillow is identical to another one with a poem dated 1204 A.D.[2] Both are products of the Cizhou kilns during the Jin dynasty.

(1)   A conventional literary allusion for praying to the gods by lighting incense and making oaths, as noted in the actions of Diao Shan, a minor female character in the *San Guo Zhi Yen Yi* (*The Romance of the Three Kingdoms*).
(2)   Not yet published.

### 88.  Stoneware Pillow in the Shape of a Reclining Baby, Decorated with a Poem, Pacun Ware
*Jin dynasty (1115–1234 A.D.)*
*H: 11.0 cm; W: 17.4 cm; L: 39.3 cm*

Pacun kilns, located in present-day Yu County, Henan Province, belonged to the group of the northern folkware ceramic kilns of the Song dynasty. They produced many different kinds of wares with a black decor on a white ground. Ceramic pillows were much in vogue during the Song dynasty, but those that the Pacun kilns made in the shape of children had a special flavor. For instance, the top of this pillow in the shape of a reclining baby girl bears two poems in running cursive script, both starting from the middle of the pillow. They read:

> "Leaves are falling, apes howling, and frost fills the sky.
> On the other side of the river, an old fisherman closes his weary eyes."

This is taken from the poem "A Night Mooring at Maple Tree Bridge" by the famous Tang poet Zhang Ji,[1] but the wording is erroneous. The original poem reads:

> "The moon is setting, a crow cawing, and frost fills the sky.
> In the river maples, the fishermen's fires blink wearily at one another."

Natural and unaffected, this child-shaped pillow is a very refreshing and lively note.

(1)   张继 (765–830? A.D.)

### 89.  Pottery Pillow with Colored Glazes and Incised Decoration of Flowers and Birds (Colorplate XXVII)
*Jin dynasty (1115–1234 A.D.)*
*H: 13.0 cm; W: 21.9 cm; L: 49.1 cm*

Following the tradition established by the Tang three-color wares,[1] the Song potters introduced two color glazes in red and black. The reds are deep and gorgeous; the blacks look like lacquered ink. This is unusual, as black glazes were rarely used at the time.

This pillow is decorated with an assortment of many different glazes: red, green, yellow, white, black, etc. The four sides display patterns of geometric flowers and leaves, while the top is carved and incised with a phoenix and peonies on a light yellow ground. The flying phoenix in the center has white feathers and a black head; the peony flowers are a dazzling red with green leaves. The colors are bright and shiny, yet not gaudy.

This is an outstanding product of the northern folkware kilns.

(1)   See Catalogue no. 65, footnote (1).

### 90.  Stem Cup with Shufu Glaze and Impressed Decoration of Dragons in Clouds, Jingde Ware, Porcelain
*Yuan dynasty (1271–1368 A.D.)*
*H: 13.3 cm; D (mouth): 13.8 cm; D (foot): 5.6 cm*

Shufu wares were important porcelains commissioned at the Jingdezhen kilns by the Imperial Privy Council.[1] Their bodies are delicate, finely finished yet quite strong, but with glazes that look as if they just lost their transparency. The white glaze contains a hint of blue-green and is exactly the tinge of a goose egg. Many objects are decorated with impressed designs, including some with such inscriptions as "Shufu"[2] and "Taixi."[3]

The inside of this pure white glazed stem cup, a typical example of Shufu ware, bears an impressed decoration of a pair of dragons floating among clouds.

It was excavated in 1952 in Qingpu County, Shanghai Municipality, from the Ren family tomb dating from the Yuan dynasty.

(1)   枢密院.
(2)   枢府: an abbreviation for Shumiyuan ("Privy Council").
(3)   太禧, an abbreviation for Taixiyuan, one of the government offices during the Yuan dynasty.

### 91.  Blue-and-white Porcelain Vase with Peony Scroll, Jingde Ware (Colorplate XXIX)
*Yuan dynasty (1271–1368 A.D.)*
*H: 40.1 cm; D (mouth): 6.1 cm; D (base): 13.4 cm*

The Jingde kilns were located in present-day Jingdezhen City, Jiangxi Province, and it is in these kilns that the important blue-and-white porcelains of the Yuan dynasty were produced. These porcelains went through a single high-temperature firing after the blue decor had been painted over the complete body and a transparent glaze applied.

Many differing views have been put forth, both in China and abroad, concerning the origin of blue-and-white porcelains, but there is no doubt that the underglaze cobalt blue wares made during the Tang period[1] and the blue-and-white porcelain sherds excavated from the foundation of the Jinsha Pagoda, located in Longquan County, Zhejiang Province, and dated 977 A.D., as well as from the foundation of the Huancui Pagoda, located in Shaoxing County and dated 1265 A.D.,[2] are important pieces of evidence for the study of the origin of blue-and-white porcelain.

The manufacture of Jingdezhen blue-and-white porcelains had already reached full maturity during the Yuan dynasty, as evidenced not only by many exquisite pieces excavated from Yuan period remains of dwellings, underground caches and tombs, but also by the sherds found at the Hutian kiln site in Jingdezhen.

This vase is full bodied. The main decor on the belly consists of a peony scroll, and the shoulder displays four *ruyi* lappets, where egrets and mandarin ducks arranged symmetrically in a lotus pond contrast with the blue sea waves that serve as background. This type of technique where a white space is reserved in a background of blue sea waves is similar to that found on a Yuan covered octagonal porcelain vase with a dragon and cloud decoration against blue water, excavated in Baoding, Hebei.[3]

(1)   Nanjing Museum *et al.*,
" 扬州唐城遗址 1975 年考古工作简报 " ("Yangzhou Tang cheng yizhi 1975 nian kaogu gongzuo jianbao", "Brief Report of the Archaeological Work Done during the 1975 Season at the Tang City Site at Yangzhou"), *Wenwu*, 1977, no. 9, pp. 16–30.
(2)   Zhejiang Provincial Museum,
" 浙江两处塔基出土宋青花瓷 " ("Zhejiang liangchu taji chutu Song qinghuaci", "Song Dynasty Blue-and-white Porcelain Excavated from Two Pagoda Foundations in Zhejiang"), *Wenwu*, 1980, no. 4, pp. 1–3.
(3)   See *Wenwu*, 1965, no. 2.

### 92.  Blue-and-white Porcelain Plate in the Shape of Lotus Petals, Jingde Ware (Colorplate XXX)
*Yuan dynasty (1271–1368 A.D.)*
*H: 5.6 cm; D (mouth): 29.6 cm; D (foot): 9.0 cm*

The Jingde kilns of the Yuan dynasty mastered the firing of blue-and-white porcelain, which gradually took over the dominant position in ceramic production held before the Yuan by celadons and white wares. Since then, the production of Chinese porcelain developed along the lines of painted decoration, which flourished undiminished through the Ming and Qing dynasties.

The shape of this plate is unconventional, as it consists of a group of eight lotus petals. The center displays lotus flowers and leaves, while each of the eight petals is filled with various precious symbols.[1] The design of this superb item is lax or dense, depending upon the available space, and the blue tones contrast beautifully with the white background.

(1) The eight symbols represented are the conch, peony (?), wish-granting gem, cloud, lotus, endless knot, coral and possibly the flaming pearl. These appear to be forerunners of the later standardized *babao*. See Colorplate XXXI.

### 93. Foliated Platter Decorated in Underglaze Red with a Spray of Peonies, Jingde Ware, Porcelain
*Late Yuan to early Ming (14th century A.D.)*
*H: 9.5 cm; D (mouth): 45.5 cm; D (foot): 28.2 cm*

Underglaze red is a category of porcelain painted under the glaze with copper oxide. The Tang dynasty kilns of Jiaocheng in Shanxi and Tongguan in Changsha, Hunan, as well as the Song dynasty kilns of Jun and Linru, had independently used copper as a colorant in producing red spots on white glaze, underglaze painting, copper red glazes and red splotches on blue glaze. It is precisely from such foundations that the underglaze red wares of the Jingde kilns of the Yuan dynasty took their development. Due to an inadequate proportion of copper or poor control of the reducing flame, Yuan and early Ming underglaze red porcelains remained in a pioneering stage; they frequently turned grey or black. This platter, where the red has in part faded to grey, is a good case in point. The sprays of peony in the center and cavetto of this platter retain the elaborate and overly ornate flavor of the Yuan, but the general style is more open. The leaves of the peony are no longer painted like the formal double gourd leaves of the Yuan convention, but are more spontaneously painted, expressing an entirely fresh flavor.

### 94. "Short Rest in the Shade of a Pine," Hanging Scroll on Silk
*By Wu Wei, Ming dynasty*
*L: 166.8 cm; W: 97.2 cm*

Wu Wei (1459–1508) had for sobriquets Shiying, Lufu and Ciweng and was from Jiangxia (present-day Wuchang) in Hubei Province. After a lonely and wretched childhood, at the age of 17 he drifted toward Nanjing.

Wu Wei's behavior was unusual and unrestrained. When Zhuyi, who had the title, Duke of the State of Cheng,[1] met him, he was so astonished that he said, "Isn't this an Immortal?" As he was still a young man, people called him "Small Immortal," and this became his nickname. After he joined Zhuyi's private secretariat, his reputation increased daily and his fame spread to both capitals.[2]

Toward the end of the Chenghua period,[3] Emperor Xianzong summoned him to Beijing to serve at the Renzhidian[4] with the rank of Commissary in the Embroidered Uniform Guard.[5] He loved wine and once was called into the presence of the Emperor as he was terribly drunk. He was taken in supported by a courtier, his hair disheveled, his face dirty and his shoes dragging behind him. The Emperor roared with laughter and ordered him to paint what is known as the "Pine Spring." Wu Wei spilled ink onto the silk, rubbing it and smearing it about freely. Mountain peaks and trees, billowing pines, wind and clouds appeared instantly. Seeing this, Xianzong said with great delight, "This is truly the brush of an Immortal."

Wu Wei's character was so simple and straightforward

that he was incapable of toadyism or flattery. As many of the powerful eunuchs who wanted his paintings were not given satisfaction, they discussed Wu Wei's shortcomings in front of the Emperor. Wu Wei was furious and finally left Beijing to return to Nanjing.

In the beginning of the Hongzhi period,[6] he was once again summoned to Beijing to paint. The new emperor saw his work, was delighted with it, made Wu Wei a company Commander in the Embroidered Uniform Guard[7] and also gave him a seal inscribed "Foremost Painter." Even though Wu Wei received this kind of royal treatment, he finally malingered so that he could return to Nanjing. This is where he spent most of his life, living among the people, which explains why his work has the rich flavor of life.

Wu Wei excelled in both landscapes and figure paintings. He was proficient in several brush techniques, such as the rough brush, the fine brush and the "plain outline" manner (baimiao),[8] which took after Li Gonglin's.[9] His rougher and more expressive style was at first influenced by Dai Jin[10] and then picked up the traditions of Ma Yuan[11] and Xia Gui,[12] which he amalgamated to form a personal style that is simultaneously rough and fine and characterized by a bold, unconstrained and vigorous use of the ink.

This landscape painting depicts three farmers on a lake shore in the shade of a tree. One older farmer stands with his right hand holding a hoe, his left hand pointing toward the opposite bank. He leans forward to speak to another old farmer who sits on the ground tying on his straw sandals; next to him on the ground are a basket and hoe, the basket containing bowls and chopsticks. This siesta scene also shows a younger farmer who, barefooted, dozes off with his head on a rock. It may be that he got tired and fell asleep after hurrying to bring the food. The garments of the figures fall in strong, nimble folds, beautifully conveying a sense of the roughness of the cloth. The meticulous and gentle strokes used to depict the eyebrows and hair are vivid examples of Wu Wei's talent in the baimiao technique. Adding an interesting note to the painting, a twisted pine stands in the middle, its bends and crooks strong, graceful and varied, its needles bristling and its old vines drooping. The bank and rocks in the foreground are painted with an axe-cut stroke and the mountain peaks at the right with straight strokes made with an angled brush. The pale, distant mountains rising on the left create a clever illusion of mist. The artist's brush technique and his ink tonalities vary from hard to soft, thick to thin, light to heavy, lax to dense, and yet produce an effect of concise and unconstrained unity. The plum trees which zigzag in all directions on the bank, the new sprouts which have just begun to show their tender green, the fine grass that grows luxuriantly on the slope and, below the bridge, the roaring of the stream all contribute to create the feeling of a bright country scene on a clear spring day.

( 1) 成国公: an honorific title given to a member of the imperial family.
( 2) Nanjing and Beijing.
( 3) 1465–1487.
( 4) 仁智殿: a palace building in the Imperial Compound in Beijing which may have held the studios of court painters.
( 5) 锦衣(卫). The Embroidered Uniform Guard was the personal guard of the Ming emperors, established under the Hongwu emperor (r. 1368–1398).
( 6) 1488–1505.
( 7) See footnote (5).
( 8) 白描: a style of painting done in simple outlines without shading or washes.
( 9) 李公麟 (b. ca. 1049, d. 1106).
(10) 戴进 (fl. ca. 1426–1435).
(11) 马远 (fl. ca. 1190–1240).
(12) 夏珪 (fl. ca. 1190–1240).

## 95. "Jackdaws on a Withered Tree," Hanging Scroll on Paper
*By Lin Liang, Ming dynasty*
*L: 128.8 cm; W: 32.5 cm*

Lin Liang (c. 1416–1480) had for a sobriquet Yishan and was from Nanhai in Guangdong Province. In the middle of the Tianshun period (1457–1464), he went to the court and served at the Renzhidian,[1] where he was given the rank of Commander in the Embroidered Uniform Guard.[2] Even as a youth he loved painting, and ingenious ideas fell from his brush. He was very good at painting flowers, fruits, birds and animals in simple, light colors and particularly liked doing freehand ink monochromes of birds, trees and rocks, where his bold and straightforward brush allowed him to originate and develop new forms of expression. His reputation as a painter is considerable. People speak of "Lin Liang's feathers and fur and Xia Chang's bamboo,"[3] and history books on painting often group him together with Lü Ji,[4] as in the phrase, "Lin Liang and Lü Ji have no equals under Heaven."

Robust and free, this scroll captures the expressions of two jackdaws on a branch. The artist gave way to his imagination without departing from traditional rules. The shapes of the withered tree and its clinging vines are true to life and give a marvelous impression of staunch resistance to winter. In this fine example of Lin Liang's work, the composition is terse and the style unique.

(1) See Catalogue no. 94, footnote (4).
(2) See Catalogue no. 94, footnote (5).
(3) 夏昶 (active ca. 1415).
(4) See Catalogue no. 96.

## 96. "Teals Bathing," Hanging Scroll on Silk
*By Lü Ji, Ming dynasty*
*L: 153.4 cm; W: 98.3 cm*

Lü Ji (1477–?) had for a sobriquet Tingzhen, was nicknamed Leyu (written two different ways)[1] and was from Jin (present-day Ningpo, Zhejiang Province).

He was known for his skill in making meticulous paintings of birds and flowers. In the Hongzhi period (1488–1505), he was recommended to the court, where he served at the Renzhidian[2] with the rank of Commander in the Embroidered Uniform Guard.[3] His bird-and-flower painting was first based on his study of Bian Wenjin.[4] He also had ample opportunity to copy the famous masters of the Song and Yuan dynasties, thus acquiring a foundation of Song academic painting which enabled him to break through outmoded conventions. He united meticulous drawing in outline and freehand ink applications into one organic whole, which added a new dimension to the existing modes of expression in bird-and-flower painting. He painted landscapes and figures, as well as birds and flowers, and, together with his contemporary, the renowned bird-and-flower painter Lin Liang, enjoyed a flourishing reputation exemplified in the saying, "Lin Liang and Lü Ji have no equals under Heaven."[5] He is one of the artists representing Ming academic bird-and-flower painting.

This painting depicts four teals paddling about and chasing one another in a small cove. Perched on a rock next to the cove, a white-crowned forktail bends his head and looks intently into the water as though in search of food, and the water warmly reflects the light. All this is done with a most meticulous brush and gorgeous colors. The crevices in the cliff and the rocks are done in a forceful, axe-cut stroke,[6] which brings out their hard texture, and in the fissures in the rocks a dense growth of flowers and grass, rendered with sure-handed dots and washes, adds to the impression that spring is in the air. This is truly an elegant and delightful scroll.

(1) 乐愚 and 乐渔.
(2) See Catalogue no. 94, footnote (4).
(3) See Catalogue no. 94, footnote (5).
(4) 边文进 (active ca. 1426–1435).
(5) See Catalogue no. 95.
(6) 大斧劈皴.

## 97. "Landscape in the Style of Da Chi,"[1] Hanging Scroll on Paper
*By Shen Zhou, Ming dynasty, dated 1494*
*L: 115.5 cm; W: 58.5 cm*

Shen Zhou (1427–1509), who was from Xiangcheng, Changzhou (present-day Suzhou, Jiangsu), had the sobriquet Qinan and the nickname Shitian,[2] later in life adopting another nickname, Baishiweng.[3] He started studying poetry and painting with his grandfather, father and paternal uncle as a child and later chose the Ming painter Zhao Tonglu[4] as his master. He also received instruction from the famous painters Du Qiong[5] and Liu Jue,[6] which allowed him to attain even greater accomplishments. Respecting his grandfather's instructions, he never sought an official position and devoted himself diligently to scholarship. He was widely read, studying the classics, history, philosophy and belles lettres, as well as Buddhist scriptures and Taoist works. Being of a sincere disposition and very broad-minded, he loved to make gifts, helped people in difficulty and granted every request made by his relatives and friends. As a result, his household never had much to spare. For a while, his paintings were all the rage, and painters forged his work to make money. He always behaved magnanimously toward them and did not pursue the matter.

In the early years of his painting career, he studied the Yuan masters Huang Gongwang and Wang Meng and took example from Dong Yuan and Juran of the Five Dynasties. In his later years, he was enthralled by Wu Zhen.[7] Done with a robust and steady brush, with dense ink tonalities and a vital rhythm, his landscape paintings are carefully and precisely structured. He often inscribed his works with poems which are pure and fresh. After the age of 40, he gradually began to produce large, crude and careless scrolls known as "Crude Shen," while his delicate and meticulous works are known as "Meticulous Shen." Few of these have survived and are all the more valuable.

Shen Zhou was a great traveler all his life. He visited many times the famous sites of Jiangsu and Zhejiang and never failed to portray the scenery wherever he went. He enjoyed planting flowers and bamboo to paint them from life, which explains why even with his concise brushwork he could capture the characteristics of flowers, birds and animals. He also worked at calligraphy, studying the style of Huang Tingjian,[8] and his calligraphic style is robust and remarkably stubborn.

He was one of the founding fathers of the Wu school of the Ming dynasty, and he, Wen Zhengming, Tang Yin and Qiu Ying are known collectively as the "Four Masters of the Ming."

This painting was done in 1494 when Shen Zhou was 68 years old. The scene is of an autumn mountain. Crossing a small bridge, a young lad carrying a qin[9] precedes his master, who rides his donkey on his way to visit a friend. The brushwork is solid, the lines twisted like iron wire and the ink used to make these lines is superimposed with washes of reddish-brown ink, which are deep, full-bodied and have something of the charm which permeates Wu Zhen's gloomy panoramic views. The painting conveys a sense of abundance without crudeness and of open-heartedness and refinement.

It is because Shen Zhou had mastered the strong points of all the Yuan artists that he was able to form his own unique style.

(1) Huang Gongwang (1269–1354).
(2) 石田.
(3) 白石翁.
(4) 赵同鲁 (1423–1503).
(5) 杜琼 (1396–1474).
(6) 刘珏 (1410–1472).
(7) 吴镇 (1280–1354).
(8) 黄庭坚 (1045–1105).
(9) The Chinese zither or lute with seven strings.

## 98. "Sitting Cross-legged in a Thatched Hut," Hanging Scroll on Paper
*By Wen Zhengming, Ming dynasty*
*L:96.1 cm; W: 29.0 cm*

Wen Zhengming (1470–1559) was originally named Bi (written two different ways)[1] and had the sobriquet Zhengming,[2] which he came to use as his name, and changed his sobriquet to Zhengzhong.[3] His nickname was Hengshan.[4]

He came from Changzhou (present-day Suzhou) in Jiangsu Province where he was born into a family of officials. His father, Wen Lin, an upright and honest official, served as prefect of Wenzhou, but died when Wen Zhengming was 16 years old, and the family gradually became impoverished.

As a youth Zhengming diligently studied poetry, literature, painting and calligraphy, receiving instruction from older artists such as Wu Kuan,[5] Li Yingzhen[6] and Shen Zhou,[7] and his reputation increased gradually.

In his 54th year, he was recommended to the capital and appointed to the Hanlin Academy,[8] where he participated in the compilation of the *Wuzong Shilu*.[9] Later his colleagues discriminated against him, and this, together with the fact that he had witnessed a great deal of corruption at the court, caused him to write repeatedly to the emperor, asking permission to resign. Finally, when he was 57, his resignation was accepted, and he returned home.

After this incident, Zhengming devoted his energies to the arts of calligraphy and painting and received daily requests for his works. He was a sincere and upright man who never painted for influential officials, always displaying the noble moral integrity of the scholar.[10] His diligence in his application to the arts was unfailing until well into his eighties when he could still write perfect regular script[11] the size of a fly's head. On the day he passed away, in his 90th year, he was still able to write an epitaph for Yan Yushi's[12] mother. As soon as he finished writing, he flung away his brush and died.

Wen Zhengming was a follower of Shen Zhou,[13] but was not limited to this association. He was able to pursue his research all the way to the masters of the Song and Yuan dynasties, as in his landscape painting where he assimilated the strong points of Dong Yuan, Juran, Guo Xi, Zhao Mengfu, Huang Gongwang, Ni Zan and other artists, and fused them into his own gentle, luminous and graceful style. He painted in two distinct manners: one, which was refined, soft and intimate, using a fine brush, and the other, which was forceful and exuberant, using a rough brush. Both styles were highly regarded by his contemporaries. He also painted birds, flowers and figures admirably.

His reputation as a painter was considerable, and he attracted a crowd of students. His sons, Wen Peng and Wen Jia, and his nephew, Wen Boren, carried on his "family school", excelling at both painting and calligraphy. Great painters of the middle Ming dynasty such as Chen Chun,[14] Qian Gu,[15] Lu Shidao[16] and Lu Zhi,[17] were his students and formed a literati group with him as their leader.[18] He,

together with Shen Zhou, Tang Yin[19] and Qiu Ying,[20] were the big names of that period, and the relationship among masters, pupils and friends was excellent so that history groups them together as the "Four Masters of the Wu School".

This painting depicts a thatched hut surrounded by ancient pines that rise up to the sky. Cultivated bamboo grow in a clump, a spring babbles and in a pavilion a solitary scholar sits cross-legged on a grass mat with a boy standing in attendance to his side offering him books. As the artist himself says in the inscribed poem, "The quiet country requites my solitary grief. In the face of the wind, I search for tranquil joy."

The scene illustrates the secluded, refined life of the scholar, and the brushwork is meticulous and elegant. This is a handsome work in Wen Zhengming's meticulous style.

( 1) 璧 and 壁.
( 2) 徵明.
( 3) 徵仲.
( 4) 衡山, also a mountain in Hunan Province, one of the five sacred mountains of China.
( 5) 吴宽 (1435–1504).
( 6) 李应桢 (active second half of 15th century).
( 7) See Figure 97.
( 8) 翰林院 (Hanlin Yuan), the name of an official bureau which in the Ming dynasty was in charge of writing history and other publications.
( 9) 武宗实录, *The Official History of the Zhengde Era* (1506–1522), which had just ended prior to Wen Zhengming's appointment to the position.
(10) Scholar-painters in China did not paint for personal gain but to increase their own understanding of art and life.
(11) *Kaishu* ( 楷書 ).
(12) 严御史 : Censor Yan. See Wen Zhengming, *Futian Ji* ( 甫田集 ) and Wang Shizhen 王世贞, "Wen Xiansheng Zhuan" ( 文先生傳 ).
(13) See Catalogue no. 97.
(14) See Catalogue no. 102.
(15) 钱毅 (1508–after 1574).
(16) 陆师道 (active ca. 1538).
(17) See Catalogue no. 101, Colorplate XXXIV.
(18) This was a continuation of the Wu ( 吴 ) School, founded by Shen Zhou in Suzhou.
(19) See Catalogue no. 99, Colorplate XXXII.
(20) See Catalogue no. 100.

## 99. "Lady with a Peony," Hanging Scroll on Paper (Colorplate XXXII)
*By Tang Yin, Ming dynasty*
*L:125.9 cm; W: 57.8 cm*

Tang Yin (1470–1523) had for sobriquets Bohu and Ziwei and the nicknames Liurujushi,[1] Taohua'anzhu[2] and Taochanxianli.[3] He was from Suzhou in Jiangsu Province.

Very well versed in poetry, calligraphy and painting and especially noted as a painter, he studied painting with Zhou Chen[4] and Shen Zhou[5] and befriended such men as Wen Zhengming,[6] Zhu Yunming[7] and Xu Zhenqing,[8] with whom he often discussed artistic matters.

When he was 29 years old, he took first place in the provincial examinations,[9] but he was expelled from the national examinations after being implicated in a cheating incident. After the age of 30, he traveled far and wide among the famous mountains and great rivers of China and enjoyed their stunning natural beauty which played such an important role in his painting. From this point on, he devoted himself to his art, supporting himself through the sale of his work.

His landscapes are mostly in the style of the Southern Song masters Li Tang[10] and Liu Songnian[11] and also take in all kinds of Yuan techniques. He was by no means a conservative and could develop new ideas such as switching from axe-cut strokes to fine, long, clear and strong linear strokes, thus providing a unique stylistic approach. He was also skilled at figures, ladies, buildings, flowers and plants; his brush and ink can be elegant and soft, strong and sharp, and his scenery is meaningful and lively. His meticulous and freehand styles are equally refined. He, Shen Zhou, Wen Zhengming and Qiu Ying[12] are outstanding painters, known collectively as the "Four Masters of the Ming." Tang Yin wrote the *Liurujushi Quangji*.[13]

This painting, "Lady with a Peony", is a three-quarter, life-size portrait of a beautifully dressed woman. Her hair is bound into a high knot, a scarf falls from her shoulders and trails on the ground, and she wears a long robe patterned with round flowers. In one hand she holds a silk fan and grasps a branch of gorgeous peony in the other. The belt of her robe floats and flutters. She is glowing with health and radiating with vigor. This lovely and elegant work constitutes an excellent example of Tang Yin's paintings of ladies.

( 1) 六如居士: Recluse of the Six "Likes" of Comparisons—like a dream, a phantasm, a bubble, a shadow, dew and lightning.
( 2) 桃花庵主.
( 3) 逃禅仙吏.
( 4) 周臣 (ca. 1450–ca. 1535).
( 5) See Catalogue no. 97.
( 6) See Catalogue no. 98.
( 7) 祝允明.
( 8) 徐祯卿.
( 9) Former triennial examination for the second degree that tested candidates for official office on their knowledge of the Confucian Classics.
(10) 李唐 (b. 1050's–d. after 1130).
(11) 刘松年 (b. ca. 1150–d. after 1225).
(12) See Catalogue nos. 97, 98 and 100.
(13) 六如居士全集: *Tang Yin's Collected Works*. See footnote (1).

### 100. "Sitting Cross-legged at the Foot of a Mountain," Hanging Scroll on Paper
*By Qiu Ying, Ming dynasty*
L: 121.8 cm; W: 51.6 cm

Qiu Ying (?–1552) had the sobriquet Shifu, the nickname Shizhou,[1] was from Taicang in Jiangsu Province and lived for many years in Suzhou. His family was relatively poor, and he worked in his youth as a lacquer craftsman.

Even as a child he loved to paint and later received instruction from the renowned master Zhou Chen.[2] He associated with Wen Zhengming,[3] Tang Yin[4] and other painters and discussed the art of painting with them. In his middle age, he enjoyed the patronage of the great collector Xiang Yuanbian,[5] in whose house he copied ancient paintings, had the opportunity to see many famous antiquities and spent much time reflecting and studying. His copies of Tang and Song paintings looked almost genuine.

When painting, Qiu Ying was so wholly absorbed by his task that even if there was a deafening sound of drums and music outside his door, he would simply not hear it. As a result, his skill developed rapidly. His figure paintings, landscapes, bird-and-flower and ruled line paintings were all admirable. Many of his colored landscapes were blue-and-green after the manner of Zhao Boju[6] of the Song dynasty and were later described as "hair of turquoise and hair of gold, strands of red and locks of white, splendid and gorgeous."[7] He also used a relatively bold and unrestrained method which was derived from the school of Li Tang[8] of the Southern Song, an exquisite and rare technique.

This painting depicts the foot of a rocky cliff with a babbling mountain spring. A solitary old man sits cross-legged

on a level outcropping, his chest exposed, his shoes cast off. Grasping with both hands a staff that lies across his lap, he is lost in thought and at ease. The trees and rocks are done in a rough, sharp brush, while the lines of the figure are simple, flowing and very different in feeling from his usual meticulous style. In fact, this work falls stylistically between his meticulous and relaxed manners. It has been in the possession of the Ming collector Xiang Yuanbian and in that of the Qing collector Xie Songzhou.[9]

(1) 十洲 .
(2) 周臣 (ca. 1450–ca. 1535).
(3) See Catalogue no. 98.
(4) See Catalogue no. 99, Colorplate XXXII
(5) 项元汴 (1525–1590).
(6) 赵伯驹 (active 1120's, d. ca. 1162).
(7) See *Minghua Lu* ( 明画录 ) in *Meishu Congshu*, 3.7, p. 29.
(8) 李唐 (b. 1050's, d. after 1130).
(9) 谢淞洲(mid-18th century), a Qing painter and calligrapher, born in Wu, Jiangsu Province, who served in the palace during the Yungzheng era (1723–1735).

### 101. "Cloudy Peaks and a Valley Grove," Hanging Scroll on Paper (Colorplate XXXIV)
*By Lu Zhi, Ming dynasty*
L: 85.5 cm; W. 46.1 cm

Lu Zhi (1495–1576) used the sobriquet Shuping and was from Suzhou in Jiangsu Province. He was also nicknamed Baoshanzi[1] because he lived on Mt. Bao (present-day West Mountain of Lake Dongting).

He was a poor scholar who never served as an official and was of an upright, direct, free, easy and unrestrained disposition. He was also very obliging to his friends and so virtuous that he enjoyed an excellent reputation. He loved to recite poetry, write prose and was skilled in the running and regular calligraphic styles which he learned from Zhu Yunming, a famous Ming calligrapher.[2] His small regular script is especially neatly done, fine and vigorous and recalls the style of the Jin dynasty calligraphers.[3] He had a fine command of painting, which he studied with Wen Zhengming,[4] and frequently got together with artists and scholars of the Wumen area to paint, write impromptu verses and compose poems.[5]

His landscape paintings, which basically fall into the lineage of Wen Zhengming's meticulous blue-and-green style, are done in a clear, vigorous and highly personal brush. He was also skilled at painting birds and flowers from life, and contemporaries described him as "being in the tradition of Xu (Xi) and Huang (Quan)."

Lu Zhi's later life was poverty-stricken, but he still maintained the proud and lofty character of the scholar. Wearing the robes of a retired scholar, he lived as a recluse on Mt. Zhixing (in present-day southwestern Wu County in Jiangsu Province) where he cultivated chrysanthemums for his own enjoyment and lived very frugally. Once, the son of an official family who admired his work requested him to paint several paintings and, when they were done, wanted to recompense him with a great deal of money. But Lu Zhi adamantly refused, saying, "The reason I gave you my paintings is because you understand them, not because of money"—thus expressing his contentment with his poverty, as well as his respect for ideas and his disregard for money.

This painting of cloudy mountains and a valley grove is done in the blue-and-green style and is refined and elegant. The face of a cliff rises up steeply, jutting up into the sky. A mass of peaks crowd around, and the mountain looks dangerously steep. The rocks are done with washes and hacked strokes, the vigorous and sharp brush bringing out the rugged and deep forms of the cliff. White clouds wind through the mountains and the luxuriant trees are delicately and efficiently painted. In the middle of the cave, a lofty scholar sits quietly with his legs folded and wears a vermilion upper garment, which is bright and eye-catching. He occupies the center of the scroll and serves as a stong focal point. Behind him, a stream ripples along, gushing down from the spring above.

The poem inscribed at the top of the painting mentions the long-fostered wish of the artist to nourish his will in groves and streams. While this whole painting smacks of the "Literati school," it has its own unique character. It is a careful work of the artist when he was 57.

(1) 包山子.
(2) 祝允明 (1461–1527). One of the most prominent literary figures of the Ming period, particularly famous for his cursive scripts.
(3) 265–419 A.D.
(4) See Catalogue no. 98.
(5) 唱和, a favorite pastime among scholars. One person would recite a poem, and another or others would reply.

### 102. "Pomegranate and Mallow," Hanging Scroll on Silk
*By Chen Chun, Ming dynasty*
*L: 118.0 cm; W: 62.0 cm*

Chen Chun (1483–1544) used the sobriquet Daofu,[1] but came to use this as his name and changed his sobriquet to Fufu.[2] His nickname was Baiyangshanren,[3] and he was from Suzhou in Jiangsu Province, where he was born into a prosperous landlord's family. He attended the Imperial Academy but never became an official, and occupied himself with poetry,[4] calligraphy, painting and other scholarly arts.

He studied painting and calligraphy with Wen Zhengming,[5] but later broke away from his teacher's set of rules and developed his own natural, relaxed style. Wen Zhengming himself said of him, "Daofu's calligraphy and painting have taken their own way; he hardly seems to be my student any more." The two men were often together, painting and discussing poetry. They did not have a master-student relationship, but treated one another as friends.

Chen Chun's running and cursive scripts were superb, at first evoking the charm of Wen Zhengming's work and later inspired by the calligraphic ideals of Yang Ningshi[6] and Mi Fu[7] when he used his brush so that it soared and leapt like a horse galloping down a slope.

As a very skillful painter of flowers and plants, he emphasized working from life, observed his subjects with the greatest care and could capture the attitudes of the flowers and plants of the four seasons in their most minute details. In this domain, his technique inherited and further developed the freehand tradition, and his ways of applying both colors and ink were strongly distinctive. For colors, he uses a quiet, refined, boneless method with meticulous delineations, while his inks are dripping wet, graceful and charming. He also often used a few vigorous strokes to outline the shape of the flowers and splashed ink[8] for the leaves, varying his blacks from heavy to light and from dry to wet to suggest the different layers and the front and back of the leaves. He had a great influence on flower and plant paintings of the Ming and Qing dynasties.

In his middle years, he also began to paint landscapes, which he liked to do freehand in ink and with a rough brush, integrating Mi Fu's and Gao Kegong's[9] characteristics and fusing them together with his own easygoing and ingenious approach.

Chen Chun was one of the representative masters of the Wu school, and his name is often linked to that of another late Ming painter, Xu Wei,[10] as in the saying, "Qingteng and Baiyang."[11]

In this painting, "Pomegranate and Mallow," one of Chen Chun's works in color, the plants are all done with the boneless method, and the colors are applied with freshness and refinement. The pomegranate flowers seem to be complicated and confused, but are in fact very well organized, capturing the teasing moment when the pomegranate flowers are in full bloom. In painting the Taihu rock,[12] Chen Chun has drawn the outlines in ink with a slanted brush and has graded his washes to create a clever openwork effect. For the grassy platform in the forefront, he used bow-like matted strokes to bring out the flexibility and elasticity of bent grass. The strokes are piled on top of one another, which makes the grass look abundant and luxuriant. Finally, he has dabbed a bit of rich black ink on top of the indigo color, which makes the grass look even more lively.

( 1) 道复.
( 2) 复甫.
( 3) 白阳山人.
( 4) 诗词. Refers to two of the four orders of Chinese poetry.
( 5) See Catalogue no. 98.
( 6) 扬凝式 (873–957).
( 7) 米芾 (1051–1107).
( 8) 泼墨. A painting technique using ink in broad full strokes.
( 9) 高克恭 (1248–1310).
(10) 徐渭 (1521–1593).
(11) " 青藤、白阳." The phrase combines the nicknames of Xu Wei ("Green Vine") and Chen Chun ("White Poplar").
(12) See Catalogue no. 112, footnote (3).

### 103. "Fifth Month Lotus," Hanging Scroll on Paper
*By Xu Wei, Ming dynasty*
*L: 129.3 cm; W: 51.0 cm*

Xu Wei (1521–1593) had the sobriquet Wenchang, the nicknames Tianchishanren[1] and Qingtengdaoshi[2] and was from Shaoxing in Zhejiang Province. A late Ming scholar, calligrapher and painter, he described himself, saying, "For me calligraphy comes first, poetry second, literature third and painting fourth." He was the author of a study on Southern-style drama, the *Nanci Xulu*[3] and of plays, such as the *Sisheng Yuan*[4] and the *Xu Wenchang Quanji*.[5]

He was born into a family of petty officials. In his 20th year he took the first degree examinations;[6] he later attempted four times to pass the provincial examinations, but failed repeatedly. In the 37th year of the Jiajing emperor (1558), when the Viceroy of Zhejiang Province, Hu Zongxian, led his troops against the Japanese pirates,[7] he engaged Xu Wei as his secretary, and Xu Wei helped Hu Zongxian compose the *Xian Bai Lu Biao*,[8] for which he was praised by the officials of the court and the Jiajing emperor.

Assimilating the best of Chen Chun,[9] a Wu school painter of the preceding generation, Xu Wei innovated a spontaneous way of making freehand paintings of flowers and plants, and history books on painting link him to Chen Chun in the saying "Qingteng and Baiyang."[10] He has had a profound and long-lasting influence on the painting of later generations.

This painting depicts a lotus in full bloom above the water in midsummer. The unfolding, wind-blown lotus leaves are saturated with ink applied in the "broken brush-splashed ink" technique, while the veins on the backs of the leaves are done in dry strokes. This contrasts with the pure white lotus outlined in pale ink and creates a graceful and moving effect.

At the top left corner of the painting, Xu Wei has inscribed a poem which refers to a girl picking lotuses:

"Although they manage to cover Xishi's face, do they manage to cover the singing sound that fords across the leaves?"[11] It is filled with romantic feeling, and the exquisite calligraphy mixes vigor with beauty. The poem, the calligraphy and the painting complement each other and produce an unforgettable artistic effect.

( 1) 天池山人 .
( 2) 青藤道士 .
( 3) 南词叙录 : *Compendium of Southern Poetry.*
( 4) 四声猿 : *Four Cries of the Ape.*
( 5) 徐文长全集 : *The Complete Works of Xu Wenchang.*
( 6) 秀才 : *xiucai,* or "cultivated talents," successful candidate of the first degree examination, taken prior to provincial examinations. See Catalogue no. 99, footnote (9).
( 7) Hu Zongxian (1511–1565) was Supreme Commander of Zhejiang, Nanzhili, Fujian and Jiangxi in the struggle against Japanese pirates and insurgents in the mid-16th century.
( 8) 献白鹿表 : *Record of the Presentation of the White Deer.*
( 9) See Figure 102.
(10) See Catalogue no. 102, footnote (11).
(11) Xishi was a famous beauty of the 5th century B.C. whom the Prince of Yue sent to distract his rival, the Prince of Wu.

## 104. "Ruan Xiu Buying Wine," Hanging Scroll on Silk
*By Chen Hongshou, Ming dynasty*
*L: 78.3 cm; W: 27.1 cm*

Chen Hongshou (1598–1652) used the sobriquet Zhanghou and the nickname Laolian.[1] He was from Zhuji in Zhejiang Province and was born into a family of feudal bureaucrats. It is said that at the age of four he managed to paint a mural over ten feet high of Guan Yu[2] to the astonishment of onlookers. His talent in painting was appreciated by the Zhe school master Lan Ying,[3] who became his first teacher. When he was ten, Chen Hongshou went to Hangzhou to study painting, worked diligently and made a great deal of progress. At the age of 14, he hung his works on the market for sale, and they "immediately produced money." After his parents died he left home on his own, beginning what would be a profligate life. He had a strong sense of justice[4] as he had studied philosophy with the noted scholar Liu Zongzhou,[5] and although the vicissitudes of life caused him to become unruly and addicted to wine, his painting continued to improve.

During the reign of Chongzheng,[6] he was summoned to the court, where he devoted his time to copying the portraits of emperors of past dynasties. He became more and more famous as an artist, and some high officials and grandees were proud to know him, but the corruption of the imperial government and the persecutions which it exerted on gentlemen of upright character smashed his hopes of progressing in an official career. He resigned his post as a court painter and returned to Zhejiang. After the Qing army entered Zhejiang, Chen Hongshou became a Buddhist monk at the Yunmen temple in Shaoxing, where he took the names Huichi,[7] Laochi[8] and Yunmen Monk[9] and died from sickness in Shaoxing at the age of 55. He was one of the most creative artists of the late Ming and is grouped together with Cui Zizhong[10] in the saying, "Chen in the South, Cui in the North."

Chen Hongshou's multifaceted artistic talent encompassed figures, birds and flowers, as well as landscapes. While he inherited from past masters, he was also capable of bold new ideas and had a marked individual style. His figures, both male and female, are in the manner of Li Gonglin,[11] with imposing torsos and clearly delineated garments. In later years his forms were exaggerated, often with strange facial features and an exceptional flavor. In his bird-and-flower painting, he followed the Tang and Song approach of doing the contours in fine outlines and apply-

ing fresh and beautiful colors. In landscape painting, he added his personal touch to the style of Wang Meng and produced highly decorative works. He was also skilled in making models for wood prints and the illustrations that he did for the *Bogu Yezi,*[12] *Shuihu Yezi*[13] and *Xixiang Ji*[14] have survived. His calligraphy was vigorous, smooth and unique, and he authored the *Baoluntang Ji.*[15]

This painting illustrates the story of Ruan Xiu, the noted Western Jin (3rd–4th century A.D.) scholar, buying wine. According to *Shi Shuo Xin Yu*[16] and other records, Ruan Xiu was an easy-going, eccentric character who liked to go hiking, often with several hundred small cash hanging from his staff. He would go to wine shops, buy wine and drink his fill all by himself and would go back drunk. In addition, he refused to have anything to do with powerful personages.

The lines in the drapery in this painting are strong and fluid and have the feeling of drifting in the wind. The staff and the small cash are done in fine outlines, the colors of the bronze wine pot are exquisite and true to life. Even more marvelous are the emotive face and the expressive eyes. That added to the small flower on the side of his forehead and the bright red fruit hanging from his staff gives a most vivid rendering of the half-drunk, half-lucid, totally undisciplined and inconsiderate personage that was Ruan Xiu.

There is a colophon by Monk Duishan[17] on the mounting above the painting.

( 1) 老莲 .
( 2) 关羽 (b. 162 A.D.), a great general of the Minor Han (Shuhan) dynasty established in Sichuan during the Three Kingdoms. He was later worshipped as the God of War (Guandi).
( 3) 蓝瑛 (1585–1667).
( 4) In the Confucian sense of the term.
( 5) 刘宗周 . (fl. ca. 1575–1625).
( 6) R. 1628–1643.
( 7) 悔迟 .
( 8) 老迟 .
( 9) 云门僧 .
(10) 崔子忠 (d. ca. 1644).
(11) 李公麟 (b. ca. 1049, d. 1106).
(12) "博古叶子 ," game cards illustrated with historical personages from a compilation of stories published in 1653.
(13) "水浒叶子 ," game cards illustrated with characters from the novel 水浒传 (*Shuihuzhuan,* rendered in English as *Watermargin*).
(14) 西厢记 : *The Romance of the Western Chamber,* published in three different editions with illustrations by Chen Hongshou, one with a preface dated 1639.
(15) 宝纶堂集 : *Collected Writings of the Hall of Precious Silken Threads,* the collected works of Chen Hongshou, put together by his son, Chen Zi, ca. 1690.
(16) 世说新语 : *New Discourses on the Talk of the Times,* a 5th century text that records the conversations of and anecdotes about literary men of the Eastern Han, Three Kingdoms and Jin dynasty.
(17) 堆山 .

## 105. "Portrait of Zhao Shi'e," Hanging Scroll on Silk
(Colorplate XXXIII)
*By Zeng Jing, Ming dynasty, dated 1624*
*L: 126.1 cm; W: 50.9 cm*

Zeng Jing (1564–1647) used the sobriquet Pochen, was from Putian, Fujian, lived in Nanjing for a long time and became a famous portraitist. Many celebrities, such as Dong Qichang,[1] Chen Jiru,[2] Huang Daozhou,[3] Ge Yilong,[4] Chen Hongshou[5] and Huang Zongxi,[6] asked him to paint their portraits. Zeng Jing worked diligently all his life and was prolific. Even after his eyesight had begun to fail in his later years, he painted for the Buddhist monks of Niusnoushan[7] a portrait of their 81st generation patriarch.[8] As soon as he finished the piece, he dropped his brush and died.

The influence of his work on later generations was significant. He was much in vogue for a while and had a crowd of followers, foremost among whom were Xie Bin, Shen Shao, Xu Yi, Zhang Yuan[9] and others, who are collectively known as the "Pochen school."[10]

Zeng Jing strove to recreate the splendid tradition of ancient portraiture in his own work. This is why his portraits "are so good that they recapture the simple majesty of the Song painters" and "manage to bring together the souls of the brush and ink, the folds of the garments matching perfectly."[11] He emphasized spiritual likeness and advocated deep observation of his subjects as well as familiarity with them, saying, "When I meet them, I spare no effort to understand them through personal experience and forget all about them and myself,"[12] until he could "reach mature thinking and silent knowledge." Only then would he lift the brush to paint. As a result, his works often capture the natural expression of his subjects and bring forth their individual character.

Where technique is concerned, Zeng Jing assimilated the formal characteristics of Western painting with its emphasis on facial structure and volume. He would go for frameworks done in ink[13] applied in dozens of dry layers and only then would put on color. This was one step ahead of traditional figure painting with its repeated applications of overall washes of bright colors. According to the modern commentator Chen Hengke,[14] "With Pochen portraiture went into high gear." In addition, the lines of the draperies are smooth and simple, helping to set off the facial features. Zeng Jing's compositions are mostly full portraits, either standing or sitting, occasionally with settings, carefully chosen, and which Zeng Jing often leaves to other painters to complete.

Done in 1624, this painting is the portrait of Zhao Shi'e when he was 64 years old. He is shown as a man with a reserved, happy expression. Shi'e's sobriquet was Jianqing,[15] and he was from Wujiang. He received his doctorate[16] in 1601 and served successively as County Magistrate in Kuaiji and Senior Inspector for the Tribunal of Censors.[17]

Above the painting, the portrayed man wrote these words of praise, "Numerous portraits have been made of me, but they hardly compare with his. I can vouch that this painting is true to life"—which suffices to show the high esteem in which contemporaries held the artist's accomplishments. At the time, Zeng Jing was 61, and the portrait is a fine example of his work as he was entering his mature period.

( 1) See Colorplate XXXV.
( 2) 陈继儒 (1558–1639), a famous scholar, calligrapher and painter.
( 3) 黄道周 (1585–1646), a painter, poet and scholar who was killed after the fall of the Ming.
( 4) 葛一龙 (1557–1640), a painter of the Ming dynasty.
( 5) See Figure 104.
( 6) 黄宗羲 (1610–1695), one of the foremost scholars of the early Qing dynasty, generally held as the founder of the so-called Eastern Chekiang school ( 浙东学派 ).
( 7) 牛首山, located in Jiangsu Province, also called Niutoushan ( 牛头山 ).
( 8) 祖师. Many later Buddhist sects, Chan especially, preserved a pictorial lineage of their headmasters, which became sect "icons" in time.
( 9) 张远 (active late Ming to early Qing), portrait painter.
(10) 波臣派. Pochen was Zeng Jing's sobriquet.
(11) See Wu Xiu 吴修 (Qing dynasty), Qingxia Guan Lunhua

Jueju ( 青霞馆论画绝句 ), and Han Ang 韩昂 (Ming dynasty), Tuhui Baojian Xubian ( 图绘宝鉴续编 ).
(12) See Jiang Shao, Wusheng Shi Shi ( 无声诗史 ).
(13) Literally "ink bones" ( 墨骨 ).
(14) 陈衡恪. (1876–1923).
(15) 謇卿
(16) 进士, a third degree graduate. See Catalogue nos. 99, footnote (9) and 103, footnote (9).
(17) The Censorate was the top-level surveillance agency directly representing the emperor in matters such as inspecting the local governmental agencies, observing the conditions of the people and receiving complaints and petitions.

### 106. "Landscape in the Style of Dong Beiyuan,"[1] Hanging Scroll on Paper (Colorplate XXXV)
*By Dong Qichang, Ming dynasty, dated 1622*
*L: 234.5 cm; W: 101.2 cm*

Dong Qichang (1555–1636) used the sobriquet Xuanzai, the nicknames Sibai[2] and Xiangguangjushi[3] and was from Huating (present-day Songjiang County in Shanghai Municipality). His posthumous title was Wenmin.[4] In the 17th year of Wanli (1589), he received his doctorate[5] and ended up his official career as President of the Board of Rites[6] in Nanjing. He was a renowned calligrapher-painter of the late Ming, as well as a collector and connoisseur of very high standards. The Tang, Five Dynasties and Northern and Southern Song paintings which he collected and inscribed amount to no less than one hundred, and he copied these ancient masterpieces with such concentration of mind that "he would forget to sleep or eat." His calligraphy is strong and elegant and had considerable influence on his contemporaries. When the early Qing Kangxi emperor (Xuanye) fell in love with his calligraphy, it was for a while fashionable to imitate his style. He was skilled at painting landscapes, paying particular attention to the works of Dong (Yuan), Ju (ran) and the Four Great Masters of the Yuan (Huang Gongwang, Ni Zan, Wu Zhen and Wang Meng) but adding his own individuality and preferences, and the result was a personal style all at once clear, soft, bright, elegant, natural and leisurely. History books on painting make him the progenitor of the "Songjiang school" of painting.[7] In addition, his theories on painting were unusually perceptive. His *Hua Chan Shi Sui Bi*,[8] *Rong Tai Ji*[9] and *Hua Zhi*[10] are extant.

This landscape painting, with its light red washes and broad vistas, borrows from Huang Gongwang's concept of depicting range upon range of green hills, while the brush and ink work owes much to that of Dong Beiyuan's style. The lofty mountains are rendered with long, ribbon-like strokes, built up with ink washes. They look simple, vigorous, moist and produce a majestic effect. The tops of the peaks and great rocks are left unpainted, contrasting with the layer upon layer of strokes and bringing out the bright and dark areas of the rocks and their modeling. The trees are a triumph in ink harmony, each layer being clearly differentiated. They look graceful, elegant and create a breath-taking impression of beauty. They exemplify the degree of dexterity reached by Dong Qichang in handling ink tonalities. The painting was done in 1622, when Dong Qichang was 68 years old.

( 1) 董北苑, also known as Dong Yuan ( 董源 ), active 937–975.
( 2) 思白.
( 3) 香光居士.
( 4) 文敏.
( 5) 进士. See Catalogue no. 105, footnote (15).
( 6) 礼部尚书. The ministry was concerned with state ceremonies, rituals and sacrifices and also the reception of envoys from tributary states.
( 7) 松江派. During the mid-16th century, Songjiang briefly

replaced Suzhou and Hangzhou as the prominent center of pictorial activity.

( 8) 画禅室随笔: *Notes from the Room of Painting and Meditation.*
( 9) 容台集, a collection of writings.
(10) 画旨: *The Purpose of Painting.*

### 107. Two-eared Covered Jar, White Porcelain with Incised Floral Sprays, Jingde Ware
*Ming dynasty, Yongle reign (1403–1424 A.D.)*
*H (overall): 7.9 cm; D (mouth): 2.7 cm; D (base): 5.4 cm*

Yongle white porcelains have gained an all-time fame for their pure, flawless, thick and unctuous glazes. They are indeed the starting point of the highly developed *doucai*,[1] *wucai*[2] and *fencai*[3] of the Ming and Qing dynasties. Not only was the Yongle white porcelain in quest for whiteness in glaze and body, it also sought to be as thin as possible. This type of white porcelain with a thin body and lustrous glaze conveys to the viewer a "sweet" feeling, and this is why it was known as "sweet white."

The peony, pomegranate, chrysanthemum and camellia, which symbolize the Four Seasons, are incised on the body of this delicate little jar. It is an exquisite example of its type.

(1) "Opposed or contrasted" colors, a type of decoration combining underglaze blue outline and overglaze enamels.
(2) "Five colors," a type of decoration different from *doucai* in several respects, particularly in that outlines are drawn in overglaze enamels.
(3) "Pale colors," a term equivalent to our *famille rose.*

### 108. Blue-and-white Porcelain Covered Cup with Floral Design, Jingde Ware
*Ming dynasty, Xuande reign (1426–1435 A.D.)*
*H (overall): 13.5 cm; D (body): 9.8 cm; D (foot): 6.5 cm*

In evaluating Ming imperial blue-and-white porcelain, our forebears used to say: "Xuande comes first, then Chenghua, then Jiajing and then Wanli." To place Xuande blue-and-white wares at the top is not in the least exaggerated. Whether it is for their blue color, the variety of their shapes, their innovative painted decor or the regularity of their inscriptions, they almost all reach perfection.

The body of this particular object is pure, its glaze shiny and its shape dainty and elegant. The painted decoration is lively yet serene, and adroitly spaced, displaying a fairly high degree of painterly attainment.

A horizontal six-character mark painted below the mouth rim reads: "Made during the Xuande (reign) of the Great Ming."

### 109. Blue-and-white Porcelain Dish with Peony, Jingde Ware
*Ming dynasty, Xuande reign (1426–1435 A.D.)*
*H: 8.3 cm; D (mouth): 44.8 cm; D (foot): 33.8 cm*

Ming Xuande blue-and-white porcelains progressed so well from their Yuan foundation that the Xuande period has been praised as the golden age of Chinese blue-and-white porcelains. Because of the fairly high iron content in the imported *su-po-ni* blue[1] in use during that period, the blue decor is rich and has some blemishes.

The fine and smooth body of this object and its thick and lustrous glaze are characteristic of Xuande. The dish is decorated mainly with peony scrolls and with branches of various fruits and plants, including pomegranates and loquats, in the cavetto. The use of branches of fruits as a design was already current in the repertory of the Longquan kilns during the Yuan dynasty.

(1) One of the many terms designating cobalt blue obtained from foreign sources.

### 110. Red-glazed Porcelain Dish, Jingde Ware
*(Colorplate XXXVI)*
*Ming dynasty, Xuande reign (1426–1435 A.D.)*
*H: 5.2 cm; D (mouth): 20.3 cm; D (foot): 12.5 cm*

The successful firing of porcelain with bright red glazes during the Ming Yongle and Xuande reigns was an epoch-making event in the history of Chinese ceramics. The firing of such monochrome red glazes did not only require strict control of the reducing conditions, but also the exact proportion of copper, the slightest error making it impossible to obtain the ideal color.

Bright red is also known as "Ruby Red", "Sacrificial Red" and "Red as Clear as the Sky."[1] The Qing text *Nan Yao Bi Ji* states: "The 'Red as Clear as the Sky' glaze is based on a white glaze and a *macang*[2] glaze with some copper granules mixed with amethysts, an addition of *leping* greenstone[3] and a small quantity of frit. It should be fired during the coldest fall and winter months. One firing out of a hundred will come through, and this is why this glaze is unique among all glazes." Rare are the Xuande red-glazed porcelains that have been handed down through the generations.

This dish is glazed with a fresh and lustrous red on both inside and outside. The inside of the white-glazed base bears a mark in regular script within a double blue ring, which reads: "Made during the Xuande (reign) of the Great Ming."

(1) In Chinese this expression is homonymous with "Sacrificial Red."
(2) 麻仓釉, a glaze produced at Mt. Macang in Fouliang County, Jiangxi Province.
(3) 乐平绿石. Is found only on Leping Mountain in the western part of Leping County in Jiangxi Province.

### 111. Blue-and-white Porcelain Dish Decorated with the Eight Treasures, Jingde Ware (Colorplate XXXI)
*Ming dynasty, Chenghua reign (1465–1487 A.D.)*
*H: 3.6 cm; D (mouth): 19.1 cm; D (foot): 11.9 cm*

While some Chenghua blue-and-white porcelains are decorated in deep, heavy blue, the more typical and more common examples of the period are done in a characteristically light blue, a color effect obtained through the careful refining of native *pingdeng* and *shizi* cobalts,[1] whose iron content is relatively low.

The glaze of this dish is lustrous and thick, the blue fresh and keen. The inside and outside are both decorated with scrolls of lotus supporting the Eight Treasures. These symbols were already used during the Yuan on Longquan celadons and Jingdezhen albumen porcelains,[2] but at that time the sequence of the symbols was rather confused. With the Ming, however, the sequence—Wheel, Conch, Umbrella, Canopy, Flower, Jar (or Vase), Fish and Endless Knot[3]—became standardized.

(1) 平等青 and 石子青.
(2) White wares.
(3) See Catalogue no. 92, footnote (1).

### 112. Blue-and-white Porcelain Stem Cup Decorated with Figures in a Landscape, Jingde Ware
*Ming dynasty, Jiajing reign (1522–1566 A.D.)*
*H: 10.6 cm; D (mouth): 13.8 cm; D (foot): 4.0 cm*

Due to the use of the imported "Mohammedan" blue, typical Jiajing blue-and-whites came out in rich, fresh, subtle and lovely shades. This is the result of combining just the right proportions of Mohammedan blue with our own Ruizhou *shiziqing.*[1]

The color of this particular object is gorgeous and shiny. A scene from the story "Hai Wu Tian Shou"[2] is painted on the outside, while the foot is ornamented with Taihu[3] rocks, sea waves and cloud scrolls.

(1)   See Catalogue no. 111, footnote (1).

(2)   海屋添寿: "Replenishing Longevity at a Seaside House," an anecdote about a Taoist Immortal who resided on the seashore where each year the cranes would return and cry out the congratulatory phrase for long life.

(3)   One of the five great lakes of China, noted for its big rocks of unusual shape.

### 113. Openwork Porcelain Covered Box with Decoration of Lotus and Dragon in *Wucai* Enamels, Jingde Ware (Colorplate XXXVII)
*Ming dynasty, Wanli reign (1573–1620 A.D.)*
*H:11.4 cm; D (mouth): 21.3 cm; D (foot):16.7 cm*

*Wucai*[1] porcelains were made by painting high-fired white porcelain bodies with various enamels and firing them again in a muffle oven at a lower temperature. Since Ming potters had not yet discovered overglaze blue enamels, they used underglaze blue wherever blue was needed. The production of "blue-and-white *wucai*" wares where underglaze blue was combined with overglaze *wucai* enamels constituted the mainstream in Ming polychrome porcelain and reached its apex in the Wanli period.

The border of the cover and the body of this box are each decorated with a procession of four dragons, while the center of the cover contains an openwork lotus pond. The colors are superb, and the base bears an underglaze blue inscription reading, "Made during (the reign of) Wanli (of the) Great Ming."

(1)   See Catalogue no. 107, footnote (2).

### 114. Blue-and-white Porcelain Figure, Seated on an Animal and Blowing a Conch, Jingde Ware (Colorplate XXXVIII)
*Ming dynasty, Wanli reign (1573–1620 A.D.)*
*H: 26.4 cm*

Judging from the extant examples, Ming porcelain figurines were produced in quantity during the Jiajing and Wanli periods. Those of Jingdezhen are blue-and-white or with *wucai* enamels,[1] while those made at Dehua are exclusively in that white porcelain which is famous throughout the world.

This figure of a man seated on an animal's back, blowing a conch, ranks among the most remarkable porcelain figures produced at Jingdezhen. The man wears a "wind hat"[2] and a tight-sleeved, long gown buttoned under the right arm. Seated sideways on the animal's back, he holds the conch in his right hand, while his left hand clenches the hilt of his sword. His eyes pop out under the effort he makes in blowing the conch.

The glaze covering this man is white with a very light greenish-blue tinge, while the stand, conch, sword hilt, animal's body and decoration on the man's garment have received several thick applications of greyish blue color.

(1)   See Catalogue no. 107, footnote (2).

(2)   See Catalogue no. 67, footnote (2).

### 115. Procession of Honor Guard Figurines, Polychrome Pottery (Colorplate XXXIX)
*Ming dynasty (1368–1644 A.D.)*

Figurines of honor guards in procession are burial objects symbolizing the ceremonies in which the deceased took part in their lifetimes. Such figures could be made in pottery, wood and stone. Pottery soldiers and horses were already popular in the Qin and Western Han periods, and processional figures became so during the Six Dynasties.

This group of 66 polychrome glazed pottery figurines of honor guards was excavated from a Ming tomb in the vicinity of Beijing. It includes horsemen in "yellow armor;"[1] a

mounted band and mounted attendants carrying on their backs a jade girdle, a roll of documents,[2] a cap and seal of office; as well as bodyguards, female slaves, chair bearers and draught horses; a screen, a sacrificial altar, an armchair, a pair of candlesticks, an oil lamp, trunks for clothes, a bed and a wine pot.

According to the *Annals on Carriages and Garments* in the *Ming Shi*,[3] warriors began wearing "yellow armor" in 1516.[4] Therefore, this group of figurines was made after that date.

(1)   Worn over clothes like a coat, this garment consisted of a padded, sleeveless jacket with long slit tails extending to the knees and was tied at the waist by a sash.

(2)   The official records of the deceased.

(3)   *Ming Shi* ( 明史 ): *The Official History of the Ming dynasty.*

(4)   The 11th year of Zhengde.

### 116. Three-legged Incense Burner with Floral Pattern, Cloisonné
*Ming dynasty (1368–1644 A.D.)*
*H:10.9 cm; D (mouth):11.5 cm*

Cloisonné designs are made by soldering fine copper wires onto a metal base and filling the space between the *cloisons* with enamels of various colors. The piece is then fired, polished and gilded.

This vessel is inlaid with Indian lotus designs against a blue background. Although the flowers are basically the same, the colors vary in shades of red, yellow, white and green. Tendrils and small green leaves are evenly interspersed in the design; the color is rich and varied and is similar to the motifs found in silk brocades of the Ming dynasty.

### 117. Water Spurting Basin, Bronze
*Ming dynasty (1368–1644 A.D.)*
*H:14.4 cm; D (mouth): 35.5 cm; D (base): 23.0 cm*

The vessel has a shallow basin, flat bottom, wide mouth rim and two semi-circular vertical handles placed symmetrically on the mouth rim. The bottom of the basin is ornamented with four carp. Spilling from the mouths of these carp are raised lines imitating ripples of water.

When the basin is filled with clear water, a droning noise[1] can be heard as soon as the tops of the handles are rubbed with both hands. As the sound becomes louder, the surface of the water agitates and forms little drops that spurt upward, as if coming from the mouths of the carp.

Basically, this phenomenon is due to what is known in physics as resonance vibration. Any body has its own vibration frequency. Rubbing the handles causes the basin to vibrate and when the vibration frequency caused by the friction of the handles is close or equal to the vibration frequency of the walls of the basin, the walls then produce resonance vibration which increases the amplitude of the vibration frequency. By rubbing the basin, it is easy to produce a vibration frequency of 200 Hz, that is, a wavelength of four antinodes and four nodes. When the vibration waves reach the sides of the basin, they create a piling up of the incidence and reflection waves and form a standing wave. The amplitude of the four antinodes rapidly increases and causes beads of water to gush from that area, and if in making the basin, the mouths of the fish are placed purposely on the four areas of the greatest amplitude, the water will seem to spurt from these mouths.

Ming craftsmen were famous for their "rippling vessels," which were the result of their experience and ingenuity in handling the phenomenon of resonance vibration, even though they were not necessarily able to explain it in modern physics terms.

(1)   "Sound of bees" in the Chinese text.

### 118. Box with Peony Decoration, Carved Red Lacquer
*Ming dynasty, Xuande period (1426–1435 A.D.)*
*H: 9.7 cm; D: 21.8 cm*

The lid of this box, made of many layers of red lacquer, is filled with a carved decoration of peonies, camellias and chrysanthemums. These flower sprays are bushy, cut with practiced simplicity and thoroughly polished. Peonies, lotus, camellias and mallows are carved on the sides of the cover and box. Along the edge of the base, which is coated with brown lacquer, an inscription, incised and filled with powdered gold, reads: "Made during the Xuande period[1] of the Great Ming dynasty[1] (corresponding to the years 1426–1435 A.D.).

Guoyuanchang, the official lacquer factory, had already been established in Beijing during the Yongle period (1403–1424 A.D.). Here, lacquer wares were made specifically for the court. The carved lacquers of the Yongle and Xuande periods closely resemble those of the Yuan dynasty. They are all characterized by "deep carving and well-rounded smoothness." However, the later pieces usually have fewer layers of lacquer, and the style of the fine details in the decoration is different.

### 119. Aromatics Container, Bamboo
*Carved by Zhu Xiaosong*
*Ming dynasty (1368–1644 A.D.)*
*H: 16.5 cm; D: 3.7 cm*

Excavated from a Zhu family tomb in Gucun, Baoshan County, Shanghai Municipality in 1966, this aromatics container is the work of the famous Ming dynasty bamboo carver Zhu Xiaosong of Jiading.[1] It illustrates the legend of "Liu and Ruan Entering Tiantai," which tells about Liu Chen and Ruan Zhao who, toward the end of the Han dynasty (early 3rd century A.D.), went to the Tiantai mountain to collect medicinal herbs. They got lost and stayed with the Immortals who lived in the mountain. When they finally got home, they found out that seven generations had elapsed. Shown here is the scene of Liu and Ruan and the Immortals deeply involved in a game of chess under a pine tree beside the "Tiantai" cave. A deer and crane, symbolizing "stipend" and "longevity," are also depicted. A signature reading "Zhu Ying" and a square seal reading "Xiaosong"[2] are incised on the door plate marked "Tiantai." The lid and bottom of this container are made of red sandalwood decorated with a lively "Dragon Tiger design."[3] The composition and carving of this rare and precious object are both excellent.

(1) 嘉定. Jiading, one of the main centers for bamboo carving in the late Ming, was formerly in Jiangsu Province and is now Jiading County of Shanghai Municipality.

(2) 小松. Nickname of Zhu Ying ( 朱缨 ). He was the son of Zhu He (active 16th century) and father of Zhu Sansong.

(3) 螭虎. A lizard-like dragon with no horns.

### 120. Raft Cup, Rhinoceros Horn
*Carved by Bao Tiancheng*
*Ming dynasty (1368–1644 A.D.)*
*H: 9.7 cm; L: 25.5 cm*

Rhinoceros horn is a precious medicinal substance, and those of dark yellowish hue with an unctuous texture are especially treasured. It was the fashion among Ming dynasty high officials to have wine cups carved in this material.

Made for display, this piece in the shape of a raft is carved in the round. The top part shows a bearded old man holding a book and sitting among luxuriant fruit trees with his back against a craggy immortal abode. A lotus leaf and a seed pod are carved on the right side of the raft, while a double gourd ornaments the left. Beneath the raft are swirling waves. Carved among the branches is the signature "Tiancheng."[1]

(1) 天成.

### 121. Cup, Rhinoceros Horn
*Carved by Youkan*
*Ming dynasty (1368–1644 A.D.)*
*H: 9.5 cm; L: 14.9 cm; W: 11.0 cm*

This rhinoceros horn cup is carved in the shape of a plucked lotus leaf. The lotus leaf has a flaring mouth, while young leaves twist upward with the stem to form the handle. The latter has been hollowed out all the way to the base of the cup to allow the wine inside the cup to flow out through the handle. Outside the cup two lotus blossoms cuddle together on the back of the leaf, and small seed pods emerge from the stamens. Inside the cup a praying mantis clings to the stalk of a young lotus leaf. The design and execution of this cup are both superb. The inscription "Youkan"[1] is carved in seal script on the outside of the cup toward the base. This is a precious piece among the rhinoceros horn carvings.

(1) 尤侃.

### 122. "Mist and Trees by the Stream," Hanging Scroll on Paper
*By Wang Shimin, Qing dynasty, dated 1676*
*L: 130.6 cm; W: 54.1 cm*

Wang Shimin (1592–1680) used the sobriquet Xunzhi and the nicknames Yanke[1] and Xilulaoren.[2] He was from Taicang in Jiangsu Province and was born into a family of statesmen. During the Wanli reign, his grandfather, Wang Xijue, had climbed to the rank of Grand Secretary and became Minister of State.[3] Wang Shimin's father, Wang Heng, was made second-class Hanlin Compiler.[4]

In the early years of the Chongzhen emperor,[5] Wang Shimin, being the scion of an official house, was made Vice President of the Court of Imperial Sacrifices. With the advent of the Qing, he no longer served in an official capacity. Wang Shimin's family was very wealthy, and its collection contained many famous paintings and antiques. He loved to paint even as a child and was praised by Dong Qichang,[6] who personally gave him instruction. He made a comprehensive study of the painting of all the Song and Yuan masters, but especially respected the work of Huang Gongwang.

In his landscapes the forests and low hills are deep, the streams and valleys clearly demarcated. His brush was loosely elegant, but in his later years when his reputation was very high he tended toward increased strength and clarity.

In the early years of the Qing, Wu Weiye[7] had already written his song, "The Nine Friends of Painting," in which he placed Wang Shimin in the same group with the great painters of the preceding generation, such as Dong Qichang, Li Liufang and Zhang Xuezeng. The famous early Qing painters Wang Hui[8] and Wu Li[9] studied painting with him, and he was regarded as the grand old man of painting.[10] He also worked at poetry and ancient Chinese prose and was an excellent calligrapher, especially in the official script.[11] Many famous mountain temples asked him to write their name plaques. Later commentators put him together with Wang Jian,[12] Wang Hui and Wang Yuanqi[13] (Wang Shimin's grandson) and called them collectively the "Four Wangs," who, with the addition of Yun Shouping[14] and Wu Li, they called the "Six Masters of the Qing."

This painting depicts layer upon layer of peaks and ranges, a profusion of trees and dense fog. At the foot of the mountain, there is a house next to a stream with a man sitting and gazing out at the mountain scenery. The effect is one of luxuriant immensity. The rocks with their thick and light ink tonalities and layer upon layer of dry strokes are very much in the manner of Dong Yuan, Juran and Huang Gongwang. This painting was done in 1676 when the artist was 85 years old and is typical of his style.

( 1)  烟客 .
( 2)  西庐老人 .
( 3)  The Grand Secretary ( 大学士 ) assisted with the education of the heir apparent and served as general consultant to the throne.
( 4)  See Catalogue no. 98, footnote (8).
( 5)  崇祯 (1628–1644).
( 6)  See Colorplate XXXV.
( 7)  吴伟业 (1609–1671), a scholar, poet, calligrapher and landscape painter.
( 8)  See Figure 124.
( 9)  See Colorplate XL.
(10)  宗师 . Designates a master of great learning and integrity.
(11)  隶书 . An ancient, square, plain style of calligraphy current in the Han dynasty. Cf. Catalogue no. 98, footnote (11).
(12)  See Figure 123.
(13)  See Figure 125.
(14)  See Colorplate XLI.

### 123. "Streams and Mountains without End," Hanging Scroll on Paper
*By Wang Jian, Qing dynasty, dated 1675*
*L: 195.1 cm; W: 87.7 cm*

Wang Jian (1598–1677) used the sobriquet Yuanzhao, the nicknames Xiangbi[1] and Ranxiang'anzhu[2] and was from Taicang in Jiangsu Province. During the reign of the Chongzhen emperor of the Ming dynasty, he served as prefect of Lianzhou,[3] but declined all official positions after the advent of the Qing dynasty. He was a direct descendant of the famed Ming scholar Wang Shizhen, and his family's collection contained a great many famous paintings and calligraphies which he often studied and copied. He had a deep appreciation of traditional techniques and was skilled at painting landscapes, in which he was directly influenced by Dong Qichang[4] and remotely by the Song and Yuan masters. He studied Dong Yuan and Juran in such depth that he mastered their methods.

In his compositions the planes are clearly demarcated with well-balanced filled and empty spaces and with much diversity. The strokes and washes are done with a light and relaxed but well-controlled brush; the ink tonalities are rich. The general effect is virile and ponderous. Wang Jian could also paint blue-and-green landscapes[5] which are elegant and lovely. In the early years of the Qing, his name was linked to that of Shimin[6] as one of the "Six Masters of the Qing."

This painting depicts a network of ridges and hills with dense clumps of trees. The mountains contain villages, thatched cottages, bridges and a stream, all neatly arranged. This is an imitation of Huang Gongwang's style[7], hence such features as the "hemp rope"[8] and the "alum-headed" rocks,[9] but one can also vaguely discern traces of Juran. The dominant peak in the picture is forceful. That, added to the mountain spring that winds through the composition creates a sense of depth and distance. This is a good example of the monochrome landscapes made by the artist at the age of 78.

(1)  湘碧 .
(2)  染香庵主 .

(3)  Now located in Hebu and Lingshan Counties in Guangxi Province.
(4)  See Color Plate XXXV.
(5)  Landscapes with a predominance of blue and green pigments.
(6)  See figure 122.
(7)  See Catalogue no. 97, footnote (1).
(8)  披麻皴法 . Long, slightly wavy strokes resembling spread-out hemp fibers, also known as "spread-out hemp" fibers.
(9)  矾头卵石 . Rocks resembling lumps of alum.

### 124. "Wild Groves and Rushing Waterfall," Hanging Scroll on Paper
*By Wang Hui, Qing dynasty, dated 1672*
*L: 94.1 cm; W: 34.2 cm*

Wang Hui (1632–1717) used the sobriquet Shigu and the nicknames Gengyansanren,[1] Wumushanren[2] and Qinghuizhuren.[3] He was from Changshu, Jiangsu, where he was born into an old scholarly family. His grandfather and father were both good painters and, during his youth, he received instruction from his father, Wang Yunke, and the painting teacher Zhang Ke,[4] who was from the same place and with whom he studied landscape painting. Later, when the famous painter Wang Jian[5] came to Mt. Yu, Wang Hui painted a beautiful fan and asked to see him. During their chat, Wang Jian praised his talent, accepted him as a student and took him back to Taicang, where he introduced him to Wang Shimin.[6] In turn, Shimin took him along on a long trip along the great rivers of the North and South so that Wang Hui had the opportunity to see and copy many ancient masterpieces in private collections. Not only was he instructed by the two Wangs, he also studied diligently and made great progress with his painting. After the Kangxi emperor made a journey to the South, he commissioned the best artists in the empire to make a painting of his trip and put Wang Hui in charge of the project. When the painting was completed, the emperor admired it and wanted to give him an official position, but he declined and left the capital to return to the South. After this, his painting was held in high esteem; he was famous all over the empire. There was no end to the people who sought his work, and for a while his style was very fashionable.

Wang Hui's study of traditional techniques was comprehensive and thorough, and he took great pains to study the style of all Song and Yuan masters. Tradition has it that he copied Huang Gongwang's "Dwelling in the Fuchun Mountain" scroll[7] three times. He excelled at copying the work of every master and every school and could capture their styles. He himself said, "To move Song mountains with Yuan brush and ink and impart to them Tang vital rhythm, this is the Great Synthesis."[8] The paintings he completed between the ages of 40 and 60 are his most refined; they are elegant, clear, beautiful and dynamic. In his later years when he focused on Huang Gongwang, his compositions became flat, his brush and ink somewhat dry, dull and lacking in vitality. At the beginning of the Qing, Wang Hui, Wang Shimin, Wang Jian and Wang Yuanqi were collectively known as the "Four Wangs," and Wang Hui's friendship for the bird-and-flower painter Yun Shouping[9] was very deep. He had a great many students, including Yang Jin,[10] Shang Rui[11] and Li Shizhuo,[12] with whom he formed an influential painting school known as the Mt. Yu school.

This painting shows slopes with pine trees, flat ridges, peaks and rocky hills, patches of mist and a half-concealed Buddhist temple with its pagoda. The scene is deep, clear and quiet, the brushwork flowing and alert, with a relatively great number of dry strokes enhanced with light ink washes. The structure of the peaks and hills and the way they are painted are derived from Huang Gongwang and Wang Meng. The painting was done in the 11th year of Kangxi (1672) when the artist was 41 years old. It is representative of the refined style of his middle years. The top of the painting has a poem inscribed by his good friend Yun Shouping, which adds a touch of interest.

( 1)　耕烟散人.
( 2)　乌目山人.
( 3)　清晖主人.
( 4)　张珂, active during the reign of Kangxi (1662–1722).
( 5)　See Figure 123.
( 6)　See Figure 122.
( 7)　See, for instance, Sirén, *Chinese Painting*, IV, Plates 64–66.
( 8)　大成, a Neo-Confucian expression, which in this case could be interpreted as the combination of many kinds of accomplishments.
( 9)　See Colorplate XLI.
(10)　杨晋 (1644–1728).
(11)　上睿 (active 1715–1722).
(12)　李世倬 (1741) Gao Qipei (1660–1734), was from Shenyang, Liaoning.

### 125. "Landscape in the Manner of Ni Zan and Huang Gongwang," Hanging Scroll on Paper
*By Wang Yuanqi, Qing dynasty, dated 1710*
*L: 96.0 cm; W: 45.0 cm*

Wang Yuanqi (1642–1715) used the sobriquet Maojing, the nickname Lutai[1] and was from Taicang in Jiangsu Province. He received his doctorate in 1670,[2] after which he served successively as County Magistrate, Censor in the Board of Punishments, Secretary in the Supervisorate of Imperial Instruction and Senior Vice President of the Board of Finance.

His grandfather, Wang Shimin,[3] one of the famous painters of the early Qing dynasty, instructed young Yuanqi, giving him old master paintings from the family collection to copy and study. His senior clansmen, Wang Jian[4] and Wang Zhuan,[5] were also painters and often provided him with inspiration and direction. With the education he received at home and his own assiduous efforts, Wang Yuanqi progressed very rapidly and gradually became so well-known that he had the occasion to go to the Inner Court, where he was praised by the Kangxi emperor. At 59, he was ordered to authenticate the imperial collection of famous paintings and calligraphy and later was put in charge of the composition of a series of reference books on the theory and history of painting in large formats, known as the *Pei Wen Zhai Shu Hua Pu*.[6] He also was in charge of the painting of the "Imperial Birthday and Grand Ceremony" scroll[7] and enjoyed a great reputation in painting circles.

Wang Yuanqi's painting was influenced by that of his grandfather. He essentially emulated and copied the ancient masters, studying in depth the styles and techniques of all the great Song and Yuan painters and especially borrowing from Dong Yuan, Juran, Huang Gongwang and Ni Zan. He particularly venerated Huang Gongwang and strove to imitate his manner. The composition of his landscape paintings is plain but unusual, and he used the brush at will without the slightest hesitation, "having a diamond at the tip of the brush,"[8] as he himself put it. The painting style of his middle years is refined, while in his later years he favored vast expanses and boldness. His students and those who followed his approach were numerous and formed a strong and dynamic school, known as the "Lou-dong school."[9]

In this painting, the foreground with its cottages and rocky platform and the background with its verdant peaks and hills are separated by a big lake in the middle ground. Islands in the middle of the lake are connected by a bridge to the opposing shore. The composition is similar to Ni Zan's "flat perspective,"[10] and the entire painting is done with a relatively dry brush in heavy and lively strokes and with reddish-brown washes for the rocks and indigo blue for the dotting. As a whole, this painting evokes Huang Gongwang's vast vistas and the feeling of peaceful loneliness that permeates Ni Zan's work. This is a good illustration of the superb skill with which Yuanqi blended Ni's and Huang's approaches. This painting was done in the 49th year of Kangxi (1710) and is a refined work of his later years.

( 1)　麓台.
( 2)　进士. See Catalogue no. 105, footnote (15).
( 3)　See Figure 122.
( 4)　See Figure 123.
( 5)　王撰 (1623–1709), son of Wang Shimin.
( 6)　佩文斋书画谱. Encyclopedia of calligraphy and painting compiled by five scholars by order of the Kangxi emperor.
( 7)　万寿盛典图. A long commemorative scroll depicting some fifty scenes celebrating the 60th birthday of the Kangxi emperor.
( 8)　"金刚杵" "Diamond Club", a Buddhist ritual object. Used here as a metaphor for powerful brushwork.
( 9)　娄东派.
(10)　平远景. Also known as "level distance" where the space is deep, open and horizontal.

### 126. "Blue-and-green Landscape in Imitation of Zhao Mengfu," Hanging Scroll on Paper (Colorplate XL)
*By Wu Li, Qing dynasty, dated 1676*
*L: 135.0 cm; W: 48.4 cm*

Wu Li (1632–1718) was originally named Qi. His nicknames were Yushan[1] and Taoxijushi;[2] he was from Changshu in Jiangsu and lived in the northern part of the town. Apparently his family's home was the ancient dwelling of Confucius's disciple Yanyan (whose sobriquet was Ziyou), and inside one of the rooms was a well called "Mr. Yan's well" and having ink black water. This is why Wu Li named himself "The Ink Well Taoist."[3]

Wu Li descended from an official family of the Ming dynasty. As his father died early, the family gradually declined, and he sold his paintings to support himself. When he was 31 years old, his mother and his wife died in quick succession, and he went into a deep depression. Later on he converted to Catholicism and became a Jesuit novice. When Wu Li was 50, he went on a mission to Macao with the Western priest Philippe Couplet and at age 57 was ordained and took the religious name Ximan.[4] After Wu Li's conversion to Catholicism, he spent the next 30 years or so in Shanghai and Jiading as a missionary. In the 57th year of Kangxi (1718), he died in Shanghai at the age of 87 and was buried in the Jesuit cemetery at Lujiabang, outside the southern gate of Shanghai. In the summer of that year, Father Manoel Mendes erected a stele marking his tomb.

Wu Li was a renowned landscape painter of the early Qing and one of the "Six Masters of the Qing." He studied the calligraphy of Su Shi,[5] and his command of literature was very high. In painting he was instructed by Wang Jian[6] and Wang Shimin.[7] Wang Shimin was then a very famous painter and could promote young talents; he let Wu Li copy the Song and Yuan masterpieces in his family collection, which he did with his heart as well as his hand. Starting with Huang Gongwang, absorbing the strong points of Wang Meng and Wu Zhen and going through a process of assimilation and refinement, Wu Li gradually formed his own clear, composed, refined and dignified style.

In this landscape painting there are mountain peaks built up in layers, lush and luxuriant groves and trees, several stately pine trees on a flat bank, a solitary scholar who walks along with a staff and hums and a boy who follows behind carrying a qin[8] on his back. Cavities bore deeply into the mountain, and here and there are temples and houses. The general effect is one of remoteness, and the brushwork is precise. The rocks are built up with a dry brush and pale ink and then painted with clear, bright malachite. On the base of the rocks and in the sky, Wu Li uses a light brown wash to evoke the beautiful moment when the summer sun setting in the west lets out its last rays of light. Dated the 15th year of Kangxi (1676), this work was done when Wu Li was 45.

(1) 渔山 .
(2) 桃溪居士 .
(3) 墨井道人 .
(4) Chinese transliteration of Simon.
(5) 苏轼 (1036–1101). Also known as Su Dongpo, a celebrated statesman, poet, calligrapher and commentator.
(6) See Figure 123.
(7) See Figure 122.
(8) See Catalogue no. 97, footnote (10).

### 127. "Chrysanthemums and Rocks," Hanging Scroll on Silk (Colorplate XLI)
*By Yun Shouping, Qing dynasty*
*L: 146.5 cm; W: 49.7 cm*

Yun Shouping (1633–1690), originally named Ge, used the sobriquets Weida and Shouping, and as the latter sobriquet became his name, he changed his sobriquet to Zhengshu. His nicknames were Nantian,[1] Yunxiwaishi,[2] Baiyunwaishi,[3] Ouxiangsanren,[4] Dongyuancaoyi[5] and Dongyuanke.[6] He was from Wujin, Jiangsu.

Yun Shouping was born at the end of the Ming dynasty and with the advent of the Qing did not participate in the official examinations. He could write poetry and had a talent for calligraphy and painting. His poetry and prose, such as in his *Ouxiangguan Ji*[7] are refined, and he headed the "Piling Liuyi."[8] In calligraphy he studied Chu Suiliang of the Tang dynasty, and his style is elegant, clear, vigorous, leisurely and attractive.

As a child he learned landscape painting from his uncle, Yun Benchu, and later he studied the Four Great Masters of the Yuan and the Ming painters Shen Zhou[9] and Wen Zhengming.[10] His style is relaxed, clear, elegant and stern. His flower-and-plant painting adopted the boneless approach of Xu Chongsi of Northern Song and, combining it with direct observation from nature, strove vigorously to capture the "fragrances and colors of life." His brush is involved and delicate, his colors clear, quiet and refined, his shapes and spiritual approach forming a whole. At one point, he was praised as an "Immortal Made Man"[11] and had a very large following of students. In his *Guo Chao Hua Zheng Lu*, the Qing dynasty writer Zhang Geng said, "These days, no matter whether it is north or south of the river,[12] there isn't anyone who doesn't call him 'Nantian' or 'Zhengshu', and this is how the 'Changzhou school' came along."[13] History books on painting refer to his followers as the "Yun school" or the "Piling school", and Yun Shouping was one of the "Six Great Masters of the Early Qing."

This painting of chrysanthemums and rocks was done with care. In both front and back, bunches of chrysanthemums lean on rocks dynamically, each one having a different posture. Branches and leaves are clear and vigorous, the veins in the leaves distinct, the colors of

the flowers—red, yellow, purple and white—all arranged harmoniously. The pure air overcomes the viewer and makes him feel all the vigor and brightness of autumn. At the top of the painting, he has inscribed his own poem:

> "Confronting these yellow flowers, I am silent and speechless.
> The flowers' branches reach toward me as though with affection.
> Each leaf of the lean stalks carries the breath of frost.
> Each petal of the numerous flowers holds the brightness of autumn."

And the inscription reads in part: "In the depth of each autumn, I stroll about, carrying my pigments to play with nature's creations, which gives me much pleasure." This offers an idea of the importance which Nantian attached to the concept of painting from life.

( 1) 南田 .
( 2) 云溪外史 .
( 3) 白云外史 .
( 4) 瓯香散人 .
( 5) 东园草衣 .
( 6) 东园客 .
( 7) 瓯香馆集 : *Collected Writings of the Ou River Fragrance Hall*, collected by Jiang Guangxu in 1838 and published in 1844.
( 8) 毗陵六逸 : the "Six Recluses of Piling," a group of writers and poets living in Piling, Jiangsu Province.
( 9) See Figure 97.
(10) See Figure 98.
(11) 天仙化人 .
(12) i.e., north or south of the Yangzi.
(13) Changzhou is another name for Piling in Jiangsu Province. See preceding footnote (8).

### 128. "Pine and Rocks in the Yellow Sea,"[1] Hanging Scroll on Paper
*By Hongren, Qing dynasty, dated 1660*
*L: 198.7 cm; W: 81.0 cm*

Hongren (1610–1663) had for his secular surname and name Jiang Tao, the sobriquet Liuqi and was from She County, Anhui. He lost his father early in life. His family was very poor, but he studied diligently and took the examinations to become a first-degree graduate at the end of the Ming. His filial attachment to his mother was such that he sold firewood and blocks for printing books to support her. After his mother died he stopped sitting for examinations to become an official. He did not marry, but spent all his time reading and painting. When the Qing army entered Anhui, he left for Fujian, where he changed his name to Fang, taking the sobriquet Oumeng. He took refuge with the *Chan* master Guhang and shaved his head to become a monk, taking the religious name of Hongren with two different sobriquets, both pronounced Wuzhi,[2] and gave himself the nicknames Jianjiangseng[3] and Jianjiangxueren.[4] Later he returned to She County and lived in the Taipingxingguo and Wuming temples at the foot of Piyunfeng.[5] Since She County is so close to the Huangshan and Baiyue,[6] Hongren did not fail to travel to the Huangshan several times a year, sitting and lying in their midst, either painting or writing poetry, his pockets full of drafts and sketches for poems and paintings. He also went sightseeing in Xuancheng, Wuhu, Nanjing and Hangzhou. In the spring of 1663 as he was coming back from Mt. Lu and preparing to go to the Huangshan to meditate on life, he suddenly fell ill and died at the Wuming *Chan* temple on the 21st day of the 12th month. His good friend Tan Yansheng convened his students and buried him at the foot of Piyunfeng. Because Hongren had loved plum blossoms during his life, they planted more than ten trees around his grave to comply with his last wishes.

Hongren was a skillful landscapist, who also painted plum blossoms. He paid serious attention to the traditional techniques of past masters. During his travels around Weiyang (Yangzhou) and Jinling (Nanjing), when he heard of private collections containing calligraphy and painting by old masters, he would make all kinds of requests in the hope that he could borrow them for close examination. If the owner was a niggard who did not want to lend them, he would stand waiting outside the man's door already early in the morning, and, if by evening he had still not seen the paintings, he had no choice but to hurry back home. There were also collectors who, moved by his sincerity, allowed him to see their paintings and calligraphies. When he looked at fine works, he would kneel for a long time on the ground, examine them back and forth with the utmost scrutiny and would ignore the summons to dinner. It is because he assiduously and wholeheartedly studied the techniques of past masters and because he synthesized all their strong points that he could become an artist of distinction. While he started with Song masters, he later concentrated on the Four Great Masters of the Yuan, being particularly influenced by Ni Yunlin.[7] But he was not bound to Ni Yunlin and had his own creativity. He enhanced Northern Song concepts with the vital rhythm characteristic of the Yuan masters. When he painted the actual Huangshan scenery, his brush was vigorous and his vision very broad. The result looks simple and dispassionate, but is in fact lofty and profound. He acquired such an unsurpassed artistic vision by imitating not only the ancients but also creation itself.

With its overhanging cliffs, sheer precipices and old pines in fantastic postures, growing their roots in the cracks of rocks, forcefully soaring and wheeling in the air, this painting reflects the unique qualities of the Huangshan pine trees. The three little peaks below closely resemble the "Three Islands of the Penglai" in the Yellow Sea.[8] Without being thoroughly acquainted with the Huangshan through observation and experience, he could never have produced this great work. The lower left corner has the two characters *gengzi*, the cyclical date for the 17th year of the Qing emperor Shunzhi (1660). This careful painting was done in Hongren's 51st year.

(1)   Refers to Huangshan. See footnote (6) below.
(2)   无智, 无执 .
(3)   渐江僧 .
(4)   渐江学人 .
(5)   A mountain in Anhui Province.
(6)   Mountains in Anhui Province.
(7)   Also known as Ni Zan (1301–1374).
(8)   One of the famous sights at Huangshan. Refers to the legendary Penglai, or Isle of the Immortals.

### 129.   "Landscape," Hanging Scroll on Paper
*By Kuncan, Qing dynasty, dated 1661*
*L:119.6 cm; W: 52.1 cm*

Kuncan (1612–after 1692) had the sobriquet Jieqiu and the nicknames Shixi,[1] Baitu,[2] Shidaoren,[3] Candaozhe[4] and Dianzhudaoren.[5] He was from Wuling (present-day Changde) in Hunan Province, and his original surname was Liu. All his life he enjoyed studying Buddhism and at the age of 40 became a monk and roamed about to study *Chan* with eminent monks. First he lived in the Da'en monastery and later in the Mt. Niushou and Mt. Zutang monasteries, which were all Buddhist scenic spots in the region of Nanjing. This marked the beginning of a relatively quiet life and his most creative period as a painter. This is also where he spent his later years. Well-versed in *Chan* Buddhist studies and of noble character, he was highly re-

garded and admired by his contemporaries. As a painter, he had a style of his own and was a man of great attainments. Judging from the paintings of his that are still extant, he must have died after 1692.

Kuncan's landscape painting was derived from that of the Four Great Masters of the Yuan and, more particularly, that of Wang Meng. He also fully assimilated the essence of the Ming masters, such as Shen Zhou[6] and Dong Qichang,[7] but even more significant was his incisive investigations and generalizations of actual mountains and rivers, which led him to create his own special style with complicated compositions, a lush vegetation and vigorous and rich brushwork. In calligraphy he studied Yan Zhenqing[8] and transferred calligraphic methods to his painting. He used both the "bald" and "parched" brush[9] excellently and wielded his brush with vigor and pungency, always avoiding the pitfalls of toughness and intrepidity. His ink tonalities are thick and heavy, his washes built up layer upon layer, which creates a sense of extraordinary vitality. He was also good at poetry and prose and all his life painted many large-scale scrolls.

This painting was done in 1661 when the artist was 49 years old. It depicts mountain ridges in the Jiangnan region[10] in the heart of autumn. White clouds wind around, morning fog drifts by, rocks are washed with ochre and dotted with dark ink. A village rendered with a few very light brush strokes is barely visible in the distance, while in the foreground in a thatched hut, two men sit cross-legged on a rush kneeling mat[11] and chat. An old man with bamboo staff crosses the bridge to come for a visit. The scene is secluded and peaceful. It takes in the viewer and makes him feel that he could wander and live in it.

( 1)   石谿 .
( 2)   白秃 .
( 3)   石道人 .
( 4)   残道者 .
( 5)   菴住道人 .
( 6)   See Figure 97.
( 7)   See Color Plate XXXV.
( 8)   709–785. A Tang dynasty calligrapher noted for the structural discipline of his style.
( 9)   秃笔 (*tubi*) and 渴笔 (*kebi*). Brush techniques using very little or very dry ink.
(10)   Literally "south of the River." Refers to the area south of the Yangzi.
(11)   Usually made from cattail.

### 130.   "Wild Geese Among Rushes," Hanging Scroll on Paper
*By Zhu Da, Qing dynasty*
*L:147.6 cm; W: 73.8 cm*

Zhu Da (1626–1705) was born into the Ming imperial family as a direct descendant of Zhu Quan, the 16th son of Zhu Yuanzhang.[1] His father, nicknamed Chixian,[2] was a calligrapher and painter with a great reputation in the Jiangxi region. His grandfather, Duozheng, was also a skillful painter. Raised in a noble household and exposed to the artistic influence of his father's and grandfather's generations, at the age of eight Zhu Da could already compose poetry, write very good characters, carve seals and was especially talented in painting.

At the fall of the Ming, Zhu Da was barely 19. When he was 23, after suffering the destruction of his home and country, he left home, went to Mt. Fengxin,[3] shaved his head and became a monk, taking the religious name Chuanqi.[4] But he had a depression due to all this grief and before long became insane. In the 18th year of Shunzhi (1661), he returned to Nanchang and let his hair grow to become a Taoist priest. On the outskirts of Nanchang he built the Qingyunpu Taoist monastery, took the name Zhu Daolang[5] and became the director of the monastery. In order to live incognito, he used a great many aliases, such as Renwu,[6] Liangyue,[7] Poyunqiaozhe,[8] Guanyuanlaoren,[9] Geshan,[10] Xuege,[11] Lüwulü,[12] and in his later years called himself "Badashanren."[13]

Zhu Da was a master in ink painting, skilled at landscape and bird-and-flower painting, as well as calligraphy. His landscapes are the result of strong artistic concepts; wild and lonely as they look, they are still lofty and casual. In bird-and-flower painting, he inherited and developed the techniques of Lin Liang,[14] Shen Zhou and Xu Wei[15] and created his own original style characterized by concise compositions and a firm and pliant brush. In his early period his brush was rigid and strong, conveying a sense of aloofness and remoteness, but the works he did after the age of 50 gained strength due to his way of chopping his strokes into flat slices, and his art matured by the time he was 64. This is also the time when his calligraphy and painting became fashionable and his brush increasingly exuberant and grandiose. In his later years he painted the eyes of fish and birds with a "scorched ink"[16] circle for the contours and then a drop of ink for the pupil, giving a supercilious look to the birds. Often when he painted birds, he showed them with eyes half-open, clenched feet and a retracted neck, thus creating a feeling of resistance to hunger and cold and of enduring hardness through self-control. Such depictions make the viewer think that Zhu Da himself "had gone all over the world without a spare cassock, starved for food, thirsty for drink, pondering over the lost years."

This painting shows with great concision a towering rocky cliff in a mountain valley, a few reeds hanging over the water's edge and on top of the huge rock in the foreground two large wild geese. One rests with his body curled up; the other stretches his head around to look back. The plumage on their backs and stomachs, rendered with heavy and light dots and smears of moist ink, looks downy.

This is the creation of an artist who had reached a high degree of artistic condensation in his representation of reality. It is a careful work of Zhu Da's later years.

( 1) 朱元璋 (1328–1398), founder of the Ming dynasty.
( 2) 痴仙 .
( 3) In Fengxin County, Nanchang District, Jiangxi Province.
( 4) 传綮 .
( 5) 朱道朗 .
( 6) 人屋 .
( 7) 良月 .
( 8) 破云樵者 .
( 9) 灌园老人 .
(10) 个山 .
(11) 雪个 .
(12) 驴屋驴 .
(13) 八大山人 .
(14) See Figure 95.
(15) See Figure 103.
(16) 焦墨 . A fairly dry brush, dense and black, especially used to accentuate planes and contours. Cf. Catalogue no. 129, footnote (9).

### 131. "Wandering Around Mt. Huayang," Hanging Scroll on Paper (Colorplate XLII)
*By Shitao, Qing dynasty*
*L: 239.6 cm; W: 102.3 cm*

Shitao (1641–1718) had the secular surname Zhu and the given name Ruoji. He was from Quanzhou in Guangxi Province and used many different names and nicknames, including Yuanji,[1] Achang,[2] Xiazunzhe,[3] Datizi,[4] Ku-

guaheshang,[5] Qingxianyiren[6] and Lingdinglaoren.[7]

Shitao was a direct descendant of Shouqian, King of Jing-Jiang,[8] and a member of the Ming imperial family. Zanyi, King of Daoxi,[9] was his tenth-generation ancestor. His father's name was Hengjia. After the Chongzhen emperor Zhu Youjian committed suicide, the King of Fu,[10] Zhu Yousong, became regent in Nanjing but shortly thereafter, died. Hengjia named himself regent in Guilin but was killed by Qu Shisi,[11] while Shitao was still a child. After the fall of the Ming, Shitao cut his hair to become a monk and studied *Chan* with the *Chan* masters Lü'an and Benyue. Lü'an was not only erudite in Buddhist studies, he was also a skillful calligrapher and painter, well-versed in poetry and literature and was a source of inspiration for Shitao in his studies on Buddhism as well as poetry, calligraphy and painting.

During his early years Shitao lived in Xuancheng, Anhui. He and Mei Qing[12] were famous for their actual sceneries of the Huangshan[13] and were known together as the "Huangshan school." Shitao spent his middle years in Nanjing and there as well as in Yangzhou saw the Kangxi emperor, after which he lived in Beijing. In his later years, however, he settled in Yangzhou, where he sold his paintings up until his death.

Shitao excelled at landscape painting, but was also good at painting flowers and fruit, orchids and bamboo, as well as figures. He was opposed to the old routine and common practice of rigidly copying the ancients. Such utterances as, "I establish my own method," and "I seek the strangest peaks to make rough sketches of them," show that he had a highly creative mind. At the same time, he valued good traditions, and developed them to form his unique style. He had a great reputation as a painter and Wang Yuanqi[14] praised him, saying, "South of the Great River,[15] Shitao must be regarded as number one." In addition, Shitao was expert in arranging garden rocks and was the author of the *Hua Pu*.[16] His influence on the Yangzhou school and on present-day Chinese painting has been considerable.

Mt. Huayang is 35 kilometers south of Xuancheng, Anhui and its high peak extends way beyond the clouds. This painting was done as a record of Shitao's travel to the mountain. The scene is strange and grandiose. The foreground consists of green, bushy and twisted pines on the edge of a cliff, lush bamboo and trees and a rocky path leading to a secluded place. The background shows piled up peaks and hills one on top of another, and a foaming waterfall, and the middle ground a tortuous covered path. The scenery is complex and the artistic conception profound. The brushwork is meticulous and tight, pliant yet firm. The colors are clear, wet, quiet and refined. In the upper left, the artist has written a poem in seven-character verses entitled, "Made While Wandering Through Mt. Huayang." The inscription indicates that he completed the picture "on the road to Jinmen (Tianjin)." It must therefore be a work done during his middle period when he was traveling to Tianjin. It is an excellent example of Shitao's landscape painting.

( 1) 元济 .
( 2) 阿长 .
( 3) 瞎尊者 .
( 4) 大涤子: Name of his studio.
( 5) 苦瓜和尚 .
( 6) 清湘遗人 .
( 7) 零丁老人 .
( 8) 靖江王 . Hereditary position held by Shitao's family for 11 generations in Guilin.
( 9) 悼僖王 .
(10) 福王 . Princely designation held by the brother of the Chongzhen emperor with hereditary estates at Honanfu.
(11) 瞿式耜 (1590–1650), a high official of the Southern Ming

dynasty who was martyred at Guilin in 1650.

(12) 梅清 (1623–1697), Shitao's closest friend, also a famous artist of the Anhui school.

(13) 黄山 Cf. Catalogue no. 128, footnotes (1) and (6).

(14) See Figure 125.

(15) Designates the Yangzi.

(16) 画谱 : Treatise on Painting.

## 132. "Listening to the Spring in a House by the Torrent," Hanging Scroll on Silk

*By Gong Xian, Qing dynasty*
*L: 177.0 cm; W: 97.3 cm*

Gong Xian (1618–1689), also known as Qixian, used the sobriquets Banqian and Yeyi and the nicknames Banmu[1] and Chaizhangren.[2] He was from Kunshan in Jiangsu Province and grew up at the time when the Qing dynasty replaced the Ming. In the last years of the Ming, he joined the "Fushe" group[3] and, after the advent of the Qing, lived in seclusion on Mt. Qingliang near Nanjing, where he built the "Banmu Garden"[4] and was engaged in painting and writing and published the *Caoxiangtang Ji*,[5] the *Hua Jue*[6] and other works. In his later years he not only sold his paintings and calligraphy, but he also recruited painting students. He lived until his old age in Nanjing.

Gong Xian was the founder of the early Qing Jinling school of painting[7] and was also the leader of the "Eight Masters of Jinling."[8] He was skillful at painting landscapes, with definite opinions on the subject. He thought that landscape painting should come naturally and insisted that, when painting, one must express one's own feelings. He was one of the most creative painters of the Qing dynasty.

Gong Xian drew most of the material for his painting from the actual Jiangnan scenery,[9] as in this painting, "Listening to the Spring in a House by the Torrent," which depicts the beautiful mountain landscape of the region. Two thatched houses at the foot of the mountain are built close by a torrential spring that winds in zigzags and gently pours into a shallow stream. The tree trunks that stand upright or crisscross one another are rendered in varied, clear, bright and harmonious ink tonalities. The rocks are done with light and dark strokes. Through the branches in the near distance, large patches of white mist slowly soar into the air, part and meet again. The far distance consists of a piling up of mountains and peaks. A hollow adorned with houses and trees looks secluded and serene. The concept that Gong Xian expresses in this work is not one of dejection for having retired from the world but one of sympathy and praise for all the hermits who preserved their personal integrity. The composition avoids the pitfalls of set patterns; it gives an authentic, lively and very distinctive impression of the atmosphere prevailing in deep mountains.

The technique is inspired by the special characteristics of many painters, such as Dong Yuan, Juran, Wu Zhen and Shen Zhou,[10] and is expanded by Gong Xian's own originality. He was skilled at the use of "accumulated ink," wherein the trees and rocks are gone over many times with brushstrokes and washes so that the ink is thick as well as varied and the contrast between light and dark particularly strong. This allows him to express realistically the "vigorous simplicity" and "bold elegance" of mountains and streams.

(1) 半亩 .

(2) 柴丈人 .

(3) 复社 : Society for the Revival of Antiquity, during the late Ming, a ruling circle among the scholars of the Jiangnan region, which advocated government reform in order to preserve the Ming ruling house.

(4) 半亩园 .

(5) 草香堂集 : *Collected Writings of the Hall of Fragrant Grass*. An excellent manuscript copy is preserved in the Xi Xian Cultural Center. See Wang Shiqing ( 汪世清 ), "Gong Xian di *Caoxiangtang Ji*" ( 龚贤的「草香堂集」 ), *Wenwu*, no. 5, 1978, pp. 45–49.

(6) 画诀 : *Painting Secrets*, a painting manual written by Gong Xian and first published in 1776.

(7) 金陵画派 . The Jinling or Nanjing school included painters working in the style of the Ming Zhe school and in the style of Dong Qichang.

(8) 金陵八家 , i.e., Fan Chi (1616–after 1692), Xie Sun (active ca. 1679), Hu Zao (fl. 1662–1722), Kao Cen (active ca. 1672), Zou Zhe (active 1647–1679), Wu Hong (active ca. 1679), Ye Xin (active ca. 1661) and Gong Xian.

(9) See Catalogue no. 129, footnote (10).

(10) See Figure 97.

## 133. "Immortals' Palace in the Spring Mountains," Hanging Scroll on Silk

*By Yuan Jiang, Qing dynasty, dated 1710 A.D.*
*L: 218.6 cm; W: 113.2 cm*

Yuan Jiang (17th–early 18th centuries) had the sobriquet Wentao and was from Yangzhou in Jiangsu Province. He was a good landscapist and excelled at "ruled line" painting.[1] At first, he studied Qiu Ying[2] and later assimilated the methods of the Song masters. His art progressed rapidly, and in the Yongzheng period (1723–1735), he went to the Court to work as a painter. The majority of his paintings consists of palaces high in the mountains. He liked doing huge paintings and especially favored "continuous scenery scrolls" which connected to one another making gorgeous decorative displays.

In this painting, "Immortals' Palace in the Spring Mountains," the composition is planned with utmost carefulness. With his usual dexterity, the artist uses hacked outline strokes to render towering rocks on a mountain slope, and in the distance mountains rising all the way to the skies look haughty and domineering. The pines and cypresses in the foreground are dense and shady while peach blossoms in full bloom enhance the richness of this spring scene. Clouds wind around and flow against the edges of distant hills, the water is covered with scale-like ripples and the foam of breaking waves splash around. The vast immensity of the sky makes one feel that "water and sky are of one hue." A storeyed palace, done in fine "ruled line" technique, stands in front of the mountain. It has a *xieshanbaoding*[3] that sticks up on the ridge of its roof, double flying eaves, and high-finned *chiwei*.[4] There are long windows on all four sides, those in the center are open and one can lean there to enjoy the view. The palace looks spacious and bright. Host and guests sit in conversation on the top floor. The terrace is made of bricks, neatly laid out with a zigzagging railing. Some of the visitors walk to the back of the terrace to look at the water; others, dragging their staffs, stop to greet one another. A stone bridge is hidden away in the shade of the trees and two men are resting and chatting in its pavilion. By a stone stairway beneath the mountain slope one can reach a water pavilion. A man slowly climbs the stairs, leisurely and self-composed.

The inscription in the upper left places the painting in the year *gengyin*, the 49th year of the Kangxi emperor (1710). It is a fine work of the artist's most creative period.

(1) 界画 . Architectural drawing done with the aid of a ruler.

(2) See Figure 100.

(3) 歇山宝顶 . Ornament placed on the center of the ridge of a roof.

(4) 鸱尾 . See also Figure 153. Ornaments placed on the ends of roofs as charms against fire.

### 134. "Pine and Cranes," Hanging Scroll on Silk
(Colorplate XLIII)
*By Shen Quan, Qing dynasty*
*L: 225.2 cm; W: 117.7 cm*

Shen Quan (1682–after 1760) used the sobriquet Hengzhi and the nickname Nanping[1] and was from Wuxing, Zhejiang. Skilled at painting birds and flowers and quadrupeds he allied the meticulous brushwork of the Song Academy and the brilliant color techniques of Western painting to produce a uniquely naturalistic approach. His painting, with its meticulous strokes, its lively and realistic shapes and its heavy and gorgeous colors, was much admired by the court and the aristocracy. In the ninth year of Yongzheng (1731), he was invited to go to Japan to teach painting and lived there three years. His polished, elegant bird-and-flower style exerted a considerable influence in Japan. For a while he had a host of students, and his reputation spread abroad.

In this painting, the brushwork is meticulous and the colors beautifully applied. On the left, a tall pine curves upward and stretches out from the billows of the sea. The branches of the pine are contorted like a dragon; its needles are dark green and bristling, its bark mottled and old vines wind around it and hang in the most vigorous way. Two white cranes perch on the trunk of the pine—one turning his head and looking in the distance, one, extending and stretching his head out, looks at the sky and cries. The mountain peaks appear and disappear amidst the drifting clouds. The sea surges in a foam of turbulent waves. Water and sky merge into immensity, far beyond this mortal world. The painting exemplifies the saying, "Sea and mountains bring happiness and longevity; pines and cranes prolong life." It is a good piece with which to wish someone long life.

(1) 南苹.

### 135. "*Osmanthus Fragrans* and Tree Pie," Hanging Scroll on Silk
*By Hua Yan, Qing dynasty, dated 1742 A.D.*
*L: 168.9 cm; W: 99.0 cm*

Hua Yan (1682–1756) used the sobriquet Qiuyue and the nicknames Xinluoshanren,[1] Dongyuansheng,[2] Buyisheng,[3] and Ligoujushi.[4] He was from Shanghang, Fujian, resided in Hangzhou and later lived in Yangzhou for a long time.

As a child he was apprenticed to a paper making factory and already loved to paint. He was good at painting figures, landscapes, birds-and-flowers and insects, with a special talent for the latter two categories. Influenced by the painting techniques of such painters as Chen Hongshou,[5] Yun Shouping,[6] and Shitao,[7] he thought that painting from life was important, and his approach was concise, free and natural while his colors were bright, but not glossy. His bird-and-flower paintings compare favorably with those of Yun Shouping, each artist flying his own colors. He could also write poetry and gave us the *Ligou Ji*[8] and *Jietaoguan Shiji*.[9]

Done with a dry brush that is sleek and soft, Hua Yan's bird-and-flower paintings display a special style combining the minute and freehand approach as a technique which exerted a considerable influence on bird-and-flower painting after the middle of the Qing dynasty. In fact, he was one of the representatives of the Yangzhou school.[10] He could at once be heir to the great tradition of his predecessors and somewhat break through them and his creative capacity was very great.

The composition of this painting, "*Osmanthus Fragrans* and Tree Pie," is pithy. The *osmanthus* and the green bamboo lean against one another on the back of a pond. The tree pie in the tree is depicted realistically; lively and amus-

ing as it bends down to look at the waves in the water, it is absolutely true to life. The brushstrokes, dots and washes used for the trees, rocks, flowers and grasses are all very methodical. The ink shades are beautiful, while the colors lightly applied to the leaves of the trees, the flowers and plants and the waterweeds are clean and fleeting. The gentle and lively work conveys a sense of grace and tranquility. The tree pie is also known as "ribbons of longevity,"[11] a metaphor for long life and good luck. The inscription of this consummate example of Hua Yan's work dates it to the seventh year of Qianlong (1742).

( 1) 新罗山人.
( 2) 东园生.
( 3) 布衣生.
( 4) 离垢居士.
( 5) See Figure 104.
( 6) See Colorplate XLI.
( 7) See Colorplate XLII.
( 8) 离垢集: *The Free from Filth Collection of Writings.*
( 9) 解弢馆诗集. A collection of poems.
(10) 扬州画派. Unlike other local schools, the Yangzhou school of the 18th century was broad based and drew upon many young and diversified talents. They had a great influence on modern painting.
(11) A play upon words. The bird has two names, both reading *Shoudai* but using two different sets of characters. The first set means literally "ribbons," such as the ones attached to an official seal or medal, and alludes to the unusual length of the feathers in the bird's tail. The second set means literally "ribbon of longevity," a physiognomical term referring to two creases extending from the tip of the nose to the chin, again an allusion to the bird's tail.

### 136. "Plum Blossoms," Hanging Scroll on Silk
*By Jin Nong, Qing dynasty*
*L: 138.0 cm; W: 65.5 cm*

Jin Nong (1687–1764) used the sobriquets Shoumen, Sinong and Jijin and the nicknames Dongxinxiansheng,[1] Jiliushanmin[2] and Qujiangwaishi.[3] He was from Renhe (present-day Hangzhou) in Zhejiang.

Jin Nong was erudite and a man of many talents, who did poetry, calligraphy, painting and was a fine connoisseur of antiquities, as well as an avid collector. In the 13th year of Yongzheng (1735), the court founded the Boxuehongcike,[4] and the following year Jin Nong went to the capital to stand ready to apply, but was not selected. Terribly discouraged by his lack of success, he began traveling widely both North and South, after which he often resided in Yangzhou. It is only after middle age that he started painting.

Thanks to his diversified artistic background and because he had seen a great many famous masterpieces and had a rather strong foundation in calligraphy, his paintings of plum, bamboo, horses and figures were out of the ordinary and highly praised in such phrases as, "His brush takes him to the ancients" and "He has rid himself of the habits of other painters." He was one of the "Eight Eccentrics of Yangzhou." His calligraphic style was based on that of the *Tianfa Shenchan Stele*[5] and the *Guoshan Stele*,[6] out of which he created a squat style which combined the official[7] and regular[8] scripts and which he named "lacquer writing."[9] He also wrote poetry and prose and published the *Dongxin Xiansheng Ji*[10] and *Dongxin Xiansheng Zashu*.[11]

This painting is of a mesh of plum blossoms with many branches thick with buds, a delight for the heart and eye. The branches are done in a calligraphic style and with a great sense of rhythm. With their petals outlined and their stamens and pistils dotted, the plum blossoms appear in every conceivable shape, posture and angle. The variations in ink tonalities and the alternation of large and small branches vividly describe that moving moment when the plum blossoms brave the cold and open up in full bloom. The calligraphy of the inscription has classical elegance and density, and the refreshing poem heightens the poetical significance of the work.

( 1 ) 冬心先生: "Mister Winterheart," a nickname Jin Nong took at age 30 when, ill with fever, he recalled the Tang poem "Ziye Dong ge" (" 子夜冬歌," "Midnight Winter Song") whose first line reads, "Stillness and solitude enfold the winter heart."

( 2 ) 稽留山民.

( 3 ) 曲江外史.

( 4 ) An examination which was held twice: once in 1679 under the Kangxi emperor and once in 1736 under the Qianlong emperor. It was open to both officials and non-officials and took place at a fixed date in the palace. Successful candidates became members of the Imperial Academy.

( 5 ) 天发神谶碑, an inscription on stone carved in seal script, dated 276 A.D.

( 6 ) (禅)国山碑, a seal script inscription carved in stone, dated 275 A.D.

( 7 ) Official script (lishu) was developed in the Qin dynasty (221 B.C.–206 B.C.) for the drafting of official documents.

( 8 ) Regular script (kaishu) is the script most often used by the Chinese today. It was the last of the formal script types to be used, developing out of the lishu (official script) of the Han but not standardized until the Sui (581–618 A.D.) or Tang (618–906 A.D.) dynasties.

( 9 ) 漆书.

(10) 冬心先生集: Collected Works of Mister Winterheart, preface by Jin Nong dated 1733. See footnote (1) above.

(11) 冬心先生杂著: Miscellaneous Writings of Mister Winterheart. See footnote (1) above.

## 137. "Ink Lotus," Hanging Scroll on Paper
*By Li Shan, Qing dynasty, dated 1735*
*L: 125.9 cm; W: 60.9 cm*

Li Shan (1686–1764) used the sobriquet Zongyang, the nickname Futang,[1] as well as the aliases Aodaoren[2] and Momoren[3] and was from Xinghua, Jiangsu.

Li Shan studied landscape painting in his early years with Wei Lingcang, who was from the same hometown, and afterwards flower-and-plant painting in Gaoyou with his elder brother and the latter's wife. In the 50th year of the Kangxi reign (1711), he became a second-degree graduate,[4] and in the 53rd year of the emperor (1714), was appointed Court Attendant because of his artistic ability. During this period, the Kangxi emperor (Xuanye) ordered him to study painting with Jiang Tingxi.[5] Later he studied with the noted finger painter Gao Qipei and assimilated the bold and unconstrained techniques of the Ming dynasty artist Lin Liang.[6] His use of brush and ink in his bird-and-flower paintings is free and unbridled, very unlike Jiang Tingxi's "orthodox" manner. Because this approach was not tolerated in the Palace, he was dismissed and later served for many years as a district magistrate in Deng County in Shandong Province. He returned home when he resigned, often going to Yangzhou to sell his paintings and in the tenth year of Qianlong (1745), settled in Yangzhou, selling paintings there into his old age.

Li Shan advocated "setting up his own door"[7] in the art of painting. The flowers and plants that he painted freehand are done in an untrammelled and straightforward technique. He was also skilled at combining colors and ink monochrome and opened up new territory with his large freehand bird-and-flower paintings. He and Jin Nong,[8] Luo Ping,[9] Wang Sishen, Huang Shen, Gao Xiang, Zheng Xie[10] and Li Fangying are known collectively as the "Eight

Eccentrics of Yangzhou."

This ink monochrome painting of lotus was done in 1735 when the artist was 50 years old. He wielded his brush with gusto and splashed ink to his heart's content with extreme clarity and ease. This freehand ink monochrome painting, which is one of Li Shan's superb works, combines the characteristics of Xu Wei[11] and Shitao.[12]

( 1 ) 复堂.

( 2 ) 懊道人.

( 3 ) 墨磨人.

( 4 ) 举人. Candidates who successfully passed the provincial examinations and were qualified to participate in the metropolitan examinations at the capital.

( 5 ) 蒋廷锡 (1669–1732). A high official and bird-and-flower painter.

( 6 ) See Figure 95.

( 7 ) i.e., to be independent.

( 8 ) See Figure 136.

( 9 ) See Figure 139.

(10) See Figure 138.

(11) See Figure 103.

(12) See Colorplate XLII.

## 138. "Bamboo and Rocks," Hanging Scroll on Paper
*By Zheng Xie, Qing dynasty, dated 1759*
*L: 171.0 cm; W: 91.0 cm*

Zheng Xie (1693–1765) used the sobriquet Kerou, the nickname Banqiao[1] and was from Xinghua, Jiangsu. His family was extremely poor. His mother died when he was very young, and he was raised by his wet nurse. As a young boy he put all his energy into his studies, reading extensively history, poetry[2] and literature. He became a second-degree graduate[3] in the tenth year of Yongzheng (1732) and doctor[4] in the first year of Qianlong (1736). In 1742 he took up the position of district magistrate in Fan County, Shandong, and was transferred to Wei County in 1746. His administration was free of corruption, he was sensitive to the feelings of the people and did a number of beneficial things for them. For example, when he was district magistrate in Wei County, Shandong Province suffered famine year after year, and there were tragic cases of "cannibalism." Greatly distressed, Zheng Xie decided to open the granaries to relieve the disaster, thereby rescuing the people from danger. Because of this and other incidents, he was falsely accused of corruption and was dismissed from his post and from office. Zheng Xie then returned to Yangzhou, where he passed the rest of his life selling paintings and calligraphy.

Zheng Xie had many talents. He was highly successful in two kinds of poetry,[5] rhyming songs,[6] prose and calligraphy. His poetry is clear and smooth, quite a lot of it expressing his sympathy with the suffering of the people and his anger against corrupted officials. His calligraphy blends the four scripts—official, regular, running and cursive—with an admixture of stylistic features associated with orchid-and-bamboo painting to form what he himself called the "six and a half style," which has a rugged and fluttering quality quite unique at the time. He was also an excellent painter, specializing in orchids, bamboo and rocks, as well as plum blossoms and other subjects. He paid attention to direct observation of nature and would come to comprehend the diversified and lively shapes of bamboo by looking at their shadows projected by the sun and moon on his paper windows and white-washed walls. He would also observe the differences between orchids near caves and orchids grown in containers, and as a result his works are rich in life flavor and compositional variety. At the same time, he diligently studied traditional techniques, particularly those of Shitao,[7] Xu Wei[8] and Gao Qipei, combining them with his own experience, versatility and creativity. His brush is elegant and vigorous, his style fresh, free and easy. He often inscribed his works with poems expressing his own feelings, so that his painting is fraught with individual characteristics and emotional coloring. He and several other artists of the Yangzhou area are known collectively as the "Eight Eccentrics of Yangzhou."

This painting consists of several slender stalks of straight and elegant bamboo which stand next to a jagged rock. The leaves of the bamboo are done in dark and light shades of ink with one stroke to the left and one stroke to the right, thus showing the leaves from all sides. The rock is parsimoniously outlined with diluted ink and taken as a whole the painting makes an impression of quiet vigor, as expressed by the poem inscribed on the right, which reads in part: "A few bamboo leaves make many mountains as they naturally possess their own cool breeze. It is good to wait for the coming year when new shoots come forth and when the forest is all bluish-green and full of meandering turquoise clouds."

Zheng Xie's noble and upright character found sustenance in bamboo and rocks. Another poetic inscription which says, among other things, "It is when painting gets to be raw that it reaches maturity," evokes the artist's laborious progress from following the ancients to modifying their styles and bringing forth new ideas. Done when the artist was 66 years old, this work is precisely an example of his mature period.

(1) 板桥.
(2) See Catalogue no. 102, footnote (4).
(3) See Catalogue no. 137, footnote (4).
(4) See Catalogue no. 105, footnote (15).
(5) See Catalogue no. 102, footnote (4).
(6) 曲. *Qu*, or songs, first developed in the Yuan dynasty (1280–1368 A.D.) as a form of popular ballad lyrics with lines of irregular length, often used in Yuan drama, or *zaqu*.
(7) See Colorplate XLII.
(8) See Figure 103.

### 139. "Zhong Kui," Hanging Scroll on Paper
*By Luo Ping, Qing dynasty*
*L: 98.4 cm; W: 38.3 cm*

Luo Ping (1733–1799) used the sobriquet Dunfu and the nicknames Liangfeng[1] and Huazhisiseng.[2] A native of She County, Anhui, he later moved to Yangzhou. He was born into an official family, but unfortunately both his parents died prematurely, and his childhood was miserable. In the 22nd year of Qianlong (1757), the 25 year old Luo Ping requested the 71 year old master Jin Nong[3] to be his teacher. He was so talented that the old master thought highly of him, saying, "The tip of his brush is clever. It does not make the slightest error." Luo Ping studied with great diligence, rarely leaving his master, whose "footsteps [4] he dogged daily, and they would conduct their business as close relatives do." Before long he was regarded as a promising talent and became the leader of the late Yangzhou painting circles. In his old age he was a devotee of Buddhism, calling himself Yiyundaoren[5] and publishing the *Zhengxin Lu*.[6] His wife, Fang Wanyi, was also skilled at painting plum, orchid, chrysanthemum and bamboo. Her painting style was light and deliberate.

Luo Ping traveled to Beijing three times. Taking advantage of the abundant collections of antiquities in the capital, he massively absorbed the artistic accomplishments of the past in order to nourish his own art. He copied the Song masters, imitated the Four Great Masters of the Yuan and studied the work of the Ming painters Wen Zhengming[7] and Chen Hongshou[8] and the Qing painters Shitao[9] and Wang Hui.[10] He made a wide selection of the strong points of many artists and did not confine himself to any particular one. He painted figures, landscapes, flowers and plants, plum and bamboo, all marvelously, and was also skilled at painting ghosts and gods. When his "Ghosts' Delight" came out, the famous scholars of the day, such as Yuan Mei,[11] Yao Nai,[12] Qian Daxin[13] and Weng Fanggang,[14] wrote poetic colophons for it. A member of the "Eight Eccentrics of Yangzhou," Luo Ping had the most comprehensive technical skills and used the widest range of subjects in the group. He not only possessed the lavish brush and self-indulgence that characterize the Yangzhou school as a whole, but also formed his own unique style, which is marked by a certain strangeness, a clumsy subtlety and a cool far-reaching vision.

Here Zhong Kui naps after getting drunk. This legendary catcher of demons of folk mythology is not shown with his usual angry eyes and frowning brows commanding the wind and clouds, but sitting against a rock with his eyes tightly shut, serene and pleased with himself. Behind him an old pine rises to the sky, and delicate bamboo whistle with the wind. All is quiet and beautiful. The ink tonalities are light and delicate, the lines concise and smooth. The shape of the figure is precise and his expression lifelike. It is one of Luo Ping's fine extant works.

( 1) 两峰.
( 2) 花之寺僧.
( 3) See Figure 136.
( 4) Literally, "staff and footsteps."
( 5) 衣云道人.
( 6) 正信录: *Record of the True Faith.*
( 7) See Figure 98.
( 8) See Figure 104.
( 9) See Colorplate XLII.
(10) See Figure 124.
(11) 袁枚 (1716–1798), poet, literary critic and essayist.
(12) 姚鼐 (1732–1815), author and calligrapher.
(13) 钱大昕 (1728–1804), the head of the Zhongshan Academy ( 钟山书院 ) and the Loudong Academy ( 娄东书院 ).
(14) 翁方纲 (1733–1818), a reader in the Hanlin Academy and an authority on inscriptions on stone and bronze.

### 140. "Loquats," Hanging Scroll on Paper
*By Xugu, Qing dynasty, dated 1895*
*L: 148.7 cm; W: 80.0 cm*

Xugu's (1823–1896) secular surname and name were Zhu Huairen, and he used the nickname Ziyangshanmin.[1] He was from She County, Anhui.

In his early years, he served as a lieutenant colonel in the Qing imperial army, but later resigned his commission to become a Buddhist monk. However, he would not "be vegetarian or worship the Buddha" and just had fun painting and writing calligraphy. He often visited the region of Shanghai, Suzhou and Yangzhou, selling paintings to support himself. As he said in a poem, "In my leisure I made 3,000 scrolls and begged among the people for money to eat."[2] He would stay several months in Shanghai, people would come together in crowds to ask for his works and he would leave when he was tired of painting.

He was acquainted with quite a few contemporary calligraphers and painters, such as Ren Bonian, Gao Yongzhi, Gu Heyi, Wu Changshuo, Ni Mogeng,[3] who discussed painting with him. He died in the 22nd year of Guangxu (1896) in the Guandi temple in western Shanghai at the age of 74, and when Tian'an, the abbot of the Shilin temple in Suzhou, learned that his teacher and co-religionist had passed away, he made a special trip to Shanghai to bring his coffin back to Suzhou and bury him in the Guangfu Cliff[4] on the shore of Lake Tai.

Xugu was an excellent painter of landscapes, flowers and plants, vegetables and fruits, birds and fish. He was fond of long, pointed brushes made of goat's hair and used them nimbly. Gu Heyi,[5] commenting on it, said that his style "was simple but not dry, dense but not confused." He was especially good at painting squirrels, goldfish and other animals in a "broken brush" technique[6] and in a swift freehand way that made them look very lively. Xugu dared to smash the bonds of stale methods, "blasting the past with one punch to make way for the present" and thus displaying his originality. He enjoyed a great reputation in the late Qing painting circles of Shanghai. He could also write poems, of which the *Xugu Heshang Shilu*[7] have survived.

In this loquat tree, branches reach upward unevenly and with a profusion of elegant leaves and tasty fruits. The depiction is at once realistic and lively. Done with the slanting tip of a dry brush, the painting reflects the sternness and novelty of the artist's unique style. The inscription reads, "Made in the third month, spring of 1895, in the Juefei monastery by Xugu in his 73rd year." The painting is representative of the artist's later works.

(1) 紫阳山民 .
(2) Which means that he sold his paintings for a living.
(3) Ren Bonian (see Figure 141), Gao Yongzhi (1850–1921), Gu Heyi (Gu Linshi, 1865–1929), Wu Changshuo (see Figure 156) and Ni Mogeng (Ni Tian, 1855–1919).
(4) 光福石壁 , in Guangfu Zhen, Wu County, Jiangsu.
(5) See footnote (3) above.
(6) 破笔 , *pobi* or "broken brush," where the hairs of the brush are allowed to separate from one another to produce a rough, broken stroke.
(7) 虚谷和尚诗录 : *Record of the Poems of the Buddhist Priest Xugu*, published posthumously.

### 141. "Fisherman," Hanging Scroll on Paper
*By Ren Yi, Qing dynasty, dated 1892*
*L: 183.5 cm; W: 47.0 cm*

Ren Yi (1840–1896) was first named Run and had the sobriquet Xiaolou, which he later changed to Bonian. He was from Shaoxing, Zhejiang. His father, Hesheng, was a portraitist and Ren Yi was strongly influenced by him during his boyhood. At an early age he could already do portraits from memory of the guests who often came to visit his family, thus demonstrating a talent for painting. He could also make molded images of clay.

In his early teens, Ren Yi was apprentice in a fan shop and was later discovered by the noted painter Ren Xiong,[1] who took him as his student. His painting then began to progress rapidly and before being much advanced in years he was already well known north and south of the Great River.[2] Over the years he held temporary residence in Shanghai, where he sold paintings to support himself and left behind a great number of works. His bird-and-flower painting follows the manner of Chen Hongshou[3] and Hua Yan,[4] but by adding his own modifications, he created a fresh and graceful style. His animal paintings are true to life. The story goes that once as he was discussing art with a guest he suddenly disappeared, and the startled guest found out that he had just scaled the roof of the house to look at two cats fighting. It is precisely because he was so carefully observant of his subjects that his creative works are such an artful blend of spirit and form.

Ren Yi was equally good at painting figures, especially portraits. He used a plain outline technique,[5] very close in style to that of Chen Hongshou. His wide range of subjects included people from the gentry, common people, mythical figures, as well as historical and folkloric characters. His brush was terse, his expressions lively. Forceful and free

from inhibition, his landscape paintings are majestic. For all these reasons his prestige was considerable. He, Ren Xiong, Ren Xun and Ren Yu are called collectively the "Four Ren."[6]

Here, an old man, wearing a sheepskin with the fur on the outside and holding a fishing pole, stands on a river bank, showing his back, turning his head and staring. The bank is neat and tidy. The river is a blank, conveying a sense of cold desolation. The sparse use of brush and ink, as well as the light washes and pale smears, bring out the fisherman's quiet and relaxed expression in a most moving way. This is an exquisite work of Ren Yi's 53rd year.

(1) 任熊 (1820–1857), older brother of Ren Xun and father of Ren Yu. See footnote (6) below.
(2) i.e., the Yangzi River.
(3) See Figure 104.
(4) See Figure 135.
(5) 白描 . Refer to Catalogue no. 94, footnote (8).
(6) 四任 . Ren Xiong, Ren Xun (1835–1893), Ren Yi and Ren Yu (1853–1901). The Four Ren were most important in influencing the "Shanghai School" or Haipai (海派) that arose in the late 19th century.

### 142. Small Vase, Kidney Bean Red[1] Glazed Jingde Ware
*Qing dynasty, Kangxi reign (1662–1722 A.D.)*
*H: 20.9 cm; D (belly): 8.7 cm; D (mouth): 5.2 cm;*
*D (foot): 4.2 cm*

Kidney bean red, a light-colored copper red glaze, is a creation of the Kangxi period. It is named after the kidney bean because it has the same red hue with spots of moss green. When *Nan Yao Bi Ji*[2] says, "Blown green and blown red glazes are innovations of the period," the "blown red" in question refers to this particular glaze. To fire this kind of glaze with success is extremely difficult and the finished pieces are highly valued. Less than a foot in height, most of these vessels were made to be used in studios at the Imperial Palace.

The vase has a long neck, a slightly everted mouth rim and a decoration of chrysanthemum petals on the lower part of the body. On the bottom, painted in underglaze blue and in regular script, a three-line, six-character inscription reads: "Made during the Kangxi (reign) of the Great Qing."[3]

(1) Peach bloom glaze.
(2) 南窑笔记 : *Records on the Southern Kilns* by an unknown author in the Qing dynasty.
(3) 大清康熙年制 .

### 143. Porcelain Vase with Decoration in *Wucai* Enamels Illustrating an Episode from the *Romance of the Three Kingdoms*, Jingde Ware (Colorplate XLIV)
*Qing dynasty, Kangxi reign (1662–1722 A.D.)*
*H: 43.5 cm; D (mouth): 13.5 cm; D (foot): 15.8 cm*

It is during the Kangxi period that the way of replacing underglaze blue with overglaze blue was found. This is how the pure overglaze five-color enamels took precedence over Ming five-color enamels with underglaze blue. Beside those of the official kilns, the folk kilns also produced excellent five-color porcelains, and since these kilns were not bound by the restrictions imposed by the court, the shape and decorative themes of their vessels were richer and more colorful than those of their official counterparts.

One of the most popular shapes of the Kangxi period, this vase depicts the episode of Zhao Yun rescuing his master at Changbanpo.[1] It is a fine, lively, as well as colorful depiction. This type of pictorial representation based on novels and dramas is widespread in folk porcelain and is obviously closely related to the woodblock prints illustrating the operatic libretti, which had been immensely popular since the Ming dynasty.

(1) 长坂坡: Chapter 41 from the *Romance of the Three Kingdoms*, in which Zhaoyun rescued the infant son of Liu Bei in a famous battle.

### 144. Porcelain Bowl with *Wucai* Enamels on a Red Ground, Jingde Ware
*Qing dynasty, Kangxi reign (1662–1722 A.D.)*
*H: 5.7 cm; D (mouth): 10.95 cm; D (foot): 4.6 cm*

Besides being painted on a white ground, Kangxi enamel wares also appear with all sorts of color backgrounds, such as yellow, green, black, coral red and beige. Among them, five-color enamels on coral red ground with the "Kangxi Imperial Manufacture"[1] mark in underglaze blue are the most valued.

This bowl is an excellent example of its type. The inside of the bowl and its foot are coated with white glaze which has the unctuosity of fat. On the outside, peonies, chrysanthemums and roses are depicted in white, blue, black and green against the coral ground. Overflowing with vigor, this piece exudes a fresh and lively feeling. The "Kangxi Imperial Manufacture" mark is written in underglaze blue on the bottom and in regular script enclosed within two circles.

(1) 康熙御制.

### 145. Porcelain Dish with *Fencai* Overglaze Enamel Decoration, Jingde Ware
*Qing dynasty, Yongzheng reign (1723–1735 A.D.)*
*H: 9.1 cm; D (mouth): 50.2 cm; D (foot): 29.9 cm*

At the end of the Kangxi period, the potters of Jingdezhen invented a new type of soft overglaze enamel known as *fencai*[1] by adding arsenic to lead glaze. During the Yongzheng period, these enamels underwent an unprecedented development, regardless of shapes, glazes or decoration.

A perfect example of its kind, this dish is decorated with a prunus branch, a camellia and a *lingzhi* fungus[2] painted in *fencai* enamels over the clear, pure white porcelain. The composition is sparse yet adequate; the colors are soft, refined and give forth a feeling of elegance. A blue underglaze mark reading "Made in the Yongzheng (period) of the Great Qing (dynasty)"[3] and written in regular script appears on the bottom of the dish.

(1) 粉彩. See Catalogue no. 107, footnote (3).
(2) *Lingzhi* fungus: *Polyporus lucidus*, a fungus grown on roots of trees, known as "fungus of immortality."
(3) 大清雍正年制.

### 146. Porcelain Vase with Gold Enamel on Red Ground, Jingde Ware "Shende Tang" mark
*Qing dynasty, Daoguang reign (1821–1850 A.D.)*
*H: 27.5 cm; D (mouth): 7.9 cm; D (foot): 8.5 cm*

Gold painted decoration on all kinds of color backgrounds was quite popular during the Jiajing period of the Ming dynasty and became even more fashionable during the Qianlong period. The shape of this vase is typical of the Daoguang period, but its overall design of auspicious symbols in gold enamel over a coral ground harks back to the wares of the Qianlong period.

The body of the vase is rich in auspicious symbols. There are swastikas,[1] *ruyi*, double carps, bats and peaches, which form rebuses such as "ten thousand things to your wish," "continuous years of plenty," "happiness vast as the sky" and "long life without boundary." This type of symbolic and auspicious design based on puns and implied meanings was widely used by the official as well as folk kilns of the Qing dynasty. The mark "*Product of the Shende Hall*,"[2] written in red and in regular script, appears on the bottom

of the piece. This is the imperial hallmark used by the Daoguang emperor.

(1) Swastikas: a motif that came with Buddhism from India. It is also a rebus for the Chinese word *wan*, or ten thousand.
(2) 慎德堂制: "The Hall of Prudent Virtue."

### 147. Vase, Cloisonné Enamel with Openwork Gilt Bronze Panels
*Qing dynasty (1644–1911 A.D.)*
*H: 30.0 cm; D (mouth): 10.5 cm; D (belly): 18.8 cm*

Shaped with accuracy, the heavy copper body of the vase is made of three parts: neck, belly and ringed foot. The neck is foliated, and the body can rotate. Four gilt bronze panels of dragon and phoenix design ornament the belly. An overall design of tendrils and lotus sprays in shades of dark and light blue, brownish red, crimson, pink, white, yellow, dark and light green, purple and black enamel enliven the light blue background. The colors are vibrant, even and sturdy; the cloisonné and the gilding are relatively thick. This superb and imposing vessel is highly decorative.

### 148. Basin with Double Fish Motif and Ring Handles, Green Jade (Colorplate XLVIII)
*Qing dynasty (1644–1911 A.D.)*
*H: 9.1 cm; D (mouth): 29.7 cm*

Carved from green jade, this basin has the shape of wide open mallow petals and is equipped with animal mask handles with loose rings. The outside of the piece is ornamented with a continuous design of symmetrical lotus flowers. The inside is plain and highly polished, while the bottom is carved with a pair of catfish among weeds. On the base are four flat feet. It is an elegant piece, executed with even and clean workmanship.

### 149. Square *Ding*, Carved Rhinoceros Horn (Colorplate XLVI)
*Qing dynasty (1644–1911 A.D.)*
*H: 18.4 cm; L (mouth): 10.8 cm; W: 8.2 cm*

Modeled after bronze prototypes of the Shang and Zhou dynasties, this square *ding* has straight ears, a deep belly and rests on four flattened legs. Fretwork surrounds the rim; dragons and animal masks ornament the body, while *kui* dragon[1] designs decorate the foot. The four corners and sides are marked by flanges. The decoration is magnificent and the carving of high virtuosity. The object is carved from one rhinoceros horn. Horns of this size are hard to come by, which further enhances the value of the piece.

(1) See Catalogue no. 49, footnote (2).

### 150. Brush Pot with Design Illustrating "Welcoming the Wild Goose," Bamboo (Colorplate XLVII)
*Carved by Wu Zhifan*
*Early Qing dynasty (1644–1795 A.D.)*
*H: 15.1 cm; D: 8.9 cm*

In the early Qing dynasty, one of the famous bamboo carvers of the Jiading school was Wu Zhifan, whose sobriquet was Luzhen and nickname Donghai Daoren.[1] He was familiar with art theory, skilled at composition, specialized in the carving of human figures and was especially known for his low-relief carving technique.

Depicted on this brush pot are two ancient pines by a stream with trunks covered by layer upon layer of crystalized bark and branches that converge to form a canopy. Beneath the tree a bare-chested, barefoot old man with his hair gathered into a knot sits directly on the ground with his feet tucked under him. His left hand rests on the ground, and his right hand holds a shoe. His uplifted head gazes at the bird flying toward him. The rendering of the plump figure is expressive, and the detailing of his garment fluid and graceful. A sense of peace permeates the composition. In the upper right, the signature carved in intaglio reads: "Made by Wu Zhifan of Chaxi." (Chaxi is now Nan-xiangzhen in Jiading County, Shanghai Municipality.) This is typical of his bamboo carvings.

(1) 东海道人.

### 151. Bamboo Carving, "Tao Yuanming Admiring Chrysanthemums" by Zheng Fujia
*Qing dynasty, Qianlong reign (1736–1795 A.D.)*
*H: 14.4 cm*

Zheng Fujia, whose sobriquet was Yongji,[1] was active in the reign of Qianlong. A native of Fujian who settled in Jiading, he was a skillful landscape painter, as well as a bamboo carver.

This piece of bamboo root carved in the round represents the Eastern Jin (317–420 A.D.) poet Tao Yuanming[2] living as a recluse after he retired from public life. The fluidity of the folds of the garment, the peaceful expression and the twisting pine with its gnarled old branches reflect a high level of excellence in bamboo carving. The artist's sobriquet, Yongji, is carved in seal script beneath the piece.

(1) 用吉.
(2) 陶渊明 (365–427 A.D.)

### 152. Sutra Cabinet, Inlaid Black Lacquer (Colorplate XLV)
*Qing dynasty (1644–1911 A.D.)*
*H: 31.0 cm; W: 35.0 cm; Depth: 21.0 cm*

Lacquer inlaid with mother-of-pearl is an important variety among the lacquers of China. Shells of different colors are cut into thin pieces, grouped according to color to form various designs and then inlaid onto the lacquer. This type of lacquer was already in vogue during the Qing dynasty.

Made of a wooden core coated with black lacquer, this piece consists of three sections: top, cabinet and base. The top consists of bats carved in openwork with a row of *ruyi* clouds[1] below. The window-shaped cabinet is where sutras were stored. Grass and leaf patterns ornament the base. The entire piece is inlaid with minute pieces of mother-of-pearl arranged in various motifs. The exquisite workmanship, minute detailing and lustrous colors make this a magnificent item.

(1) Clouds in the shape of the double-curved *ruyi* ("as you wish") sceptre.

### 153. Pavilion, Carved Red Lacquer
*Qing dynasty (1644–1911 A.D.)*
*H: 49.0 cm; W: 53.0 cm; Depth: 33.0 cm*

Bells hang from the cantilevered, upturning eaves of the two storeyed lacquer pavilion. *Chiwei*[1] ornament the ridge ends, and a flaming double gourd[2] stands in the middle of the ridge. The roof tiles are arranged in a pattern of lotus blossoms. The carved panels and each component of the balustrade itself are decorated with detailed carvings of exquisite design. The entire structure is one of dignity and elegance.

(1) 鸱尾: architectural ornaments used on the ends of roofs as charms against fire.
(2) Hulu or calabash, *Lagenaria vulgaris*. It has numerous meanings, amongst which are purity, longevity and fecundity.

### 154. Armchair with Design of "Nine Dragons Raging in the Sea," Carved Red Lacquer (Colorplate L)
*Qing dynasty (1644–1911 A.D.)*
*H: 101.0 cm; L: 85.0 cm; W: 61.0 cm*

The chair is made of wood. The back, arm rests and seat are fitted together with tenons. It is entirely of carved lacquer except for the seat. The latter is coated with red lacquer and engraved with a design of swastikas[1] filled with

powdered gold. Carved on the red lacquered recto of the chair back and on the arm rests are nine dragons of various sizes. Depicted in lively motion, they rage and frolic in the billowing waves. *Ruyi*[2] designs ornament the edges. The verso of the back is carved in low relief with 16 bats which seem to be flying freely in the clouds. In addition, extending from beneath the seat to the tip of the legs are various peony designs. This is a stately chair, beautifully ornamented and carved with consummate skill.

The motifs of dragons and clouds, peonies, swastikas, bats and *ruyi* found on this chair were frequently used on objects made for Ming and Qing courts. They all have auspicious meanings.

(1) See Catalogue no. 146, footnote (1).
(2) See Catalogue no. 152, footnote (1).

### 155. Round Table and Stools with Decoration of Figures and Flowers, Carved Red Lacquer (Colorplate LI)
*Qing dynasty (1644–1911 A.D.)*
*Table: H: 87.5 cm; D: 95.0 cm*
*Stools: H: 51.5 cm; D: 38.8 cm*

The round table consists of a wooden core coated with many layers of red carved lacquer. It has a round top, one leg in the shape of a hexagonal vase and a hexagonal base, all fitted together with tenons. The table top is decorated with three concentric bands of fretwork, alternating with four symmetrical groups of dragons, variations of the *shou* character[1] and tendril and flower designs. On the leg are "Five Old Men," peony, prunus, gardenia, chrysanthemum, nandina and camellia motifs. Flowers and tendrils cover the base. The entire table is a technical *tour de force* and its design is particularly imaginative. Besides the table, the four round stools form a set which required a considerable amount of work.

(1) 寿字纹. The character for longevity can have as many as a hundred variations.

### 156. "Peaches", Hanging Scroll on Paper
*By Wu Changshuo, Modern, dated 1915*
*L: 138.2 cm; W: 34.0 cm*

Wu Changshuo (1844–1927) was named Jun and originally used the sobriquet Xiangbu, which he changed to Changshuo. His alternate nicknames were Foulu,[1] Laofou,[2] Kutie,[3] Dalong[4] and he was from Anji County, Zhejiang. He was raised in a poor family of scholar-farmers and as his native place suffered a famine when he was 17, he left to go to Hupei and Anhui, roaming about for five years. He did not return home until he was 21, and he and his aged father then depended on each other for survival, spending their days farming and studying. He passed a make-up examination to become a first-degree graduate,[5] but then changed his mind about seeking official rank. At the age of 53, he was named to serve as the district magistrate for Andong County in Jiangsu Province (present-day Lianshui), but, after serving for only one month, resolved to leave and devote himself entirely to literary and artistic pursuits.

Wu Changshuo was one of the great calligraphers and painters of modern times. His poetry, calligraphy, painting and seal carving brim with individuality and creativity. He was expert in the Stone Drum style,[6] but he also did running and cursive calligraphies, always using the brush so vigorously that it seemed to go right through the paper. His seal carving style was first derived from that of the Zhejiang and Anhui masters and then traced its way back to the Qin and Han dynasties styles. He carved firmly with a blunt knife and his seals are simple and robust. Coming to painting rather late in life, he assimilated the strong points of Xu Wei,[7] Chen Chun,[8] Shitao,[9] Zhu Da[10] and Zhao Zhiqian and blended them with his own attainments in calligraphy and seal carving. At the same time, he was a perceptive observer of life. His brush was extremely bold and his vision grandiose. He was very careful when building up his compositions and formulating his intentions, thus reaching the point where he achieved a sort of untramelled conformity, dealing with the details but never losing a sense of the whole. He did not follow well-trodden paths in his choice of color either. He manipulated brilliant reds and greens with great virtuosity creating vivid and well-differentiated contrasts achieving a harmony of clashes and displaying a quiet charm with archaic overtones.

When painting, he paid a great deal of attention to the proper relationship between poetry, calligraphy and painting, which give dense, complex and extremely diversified works. His style still influences today's painting circles.

The composition of this painting is peculiar. A straight branch soars up as though suspended in midair, and its extremity holds large and ripe peaches gorged with juice, dazzlingly beautiful and perfectly lovely. The painting is dated to the year 1915 when Wu Changshuo was 72.

( 1) 缶庐.
( 2) 老缶.
( 3) 苦铁.
( 4) 大聋.
( 5) 秀才 : See Catalogue no. 103, footnote (6).
( 6) 石鼓文. *Shiguwen* or "Stone Drum Writing" style is based on inscriptions carved into a group of stone drums during the Warring States period (481–221 B.C.)
( 7) See Figure 103.
( 8) See Figure 102.
( 9) See Colorplate XLII.
(10) See Figure 130.

**157.　"The Quiet Delight of the Lotus Pond,"**
**Hanging Scroll on Paper** (Colorplate LII)
*By Qi Baishi, Modern, dated 1924*
*L:182.0 cm; W: 96.0 cm*

Qi Baishi (1863–1957) was originally named Chunzhi with the sobriquet Weiqing, but later changed his name to Huang, taking the sobriquet Binsheng and the nickname Baishi.[1] His other nicknames were Jieshanyinguanzhuzhe[2] and Jipinglaoren.[3]

Qi Baishi was born into a poor farming family in Xiangtan, Hunan, and already as a child was very much interested in painting. He was only able to attend one-half a year of school, after which he worked herding cattle and gathering firewood. At the age of 12 he was apprenticed to a carpenter, working during the day and painting in the evening. Later when he attained a modest reputation as a painter, he began to paint professionally. At the age of 40 he left to tour the famous mountains and great rivers of China. This changed his life and widened his field of artistic vision, and his painting gradually matured. He settled in Beijing when he was 50. Under the influence of Chen Shizeng[4] and other painters and with their support, he radically changed his style, carrying out his "reform of the declining years." He studied energetically the art of Xu Wei,[5] Chen Chun,[6] Zhu Da[7] and Shitao[8] making every effort to reach the stage when "the brush is simple and the expression full," or again "the form complete and the meaning genuine."

His paintings, no matter whether they are meticulous or freehand, depend upon a minute observation of real objects. He never stopped painting and all his life enjoyed particularly doing meticulous representations of insects, reaching the point where they looked true to life and absolutely real, but he also knew how to use the tersest brushwork to bring out with an exceeding sense of form the expression and demeanor of his subjects. Aside from this,

he was adept in drawing upon the vivid and intense colors of Chinese folk art to form his own colorful and dynamic approach. Qi Baishi's artistic accomplishments are also manifest in his poetry, calligraphy and seal carving. They illustrate fully the great deal of effort he put into art and the considerable talents with which he had been endowed.

This painting was done in 1924 when he was 62. Through ingenious arrangement of the lotus flowers, leaves and cupules, the artist gives an idea of the lively scene that a lotus pond makes in midsummer. The lotus stalks, which are depicted in thick ink, and crisscross the painting with vigor, show that the damaged lotus leaves, weak and degenerate as they are, still display an indomitable force of life, which is an excellent portrayal of the artist's later years.

(1) 白石.
(2) 借山吟馆主者.
(3) 寄萍老人.
(4) 陈师曾 or 陈衡恪 Chen Hengke. See Catalogue no. 105, footnote (13).
(5) See Figure 103.
(6) See Figure 102.
(7) See Figure 130.
(8) See Colorplate XLII.

**158.　"Landscape," Hanging Scroll on Paper**
*By Huang Binhong, Modern, dated 1946*
*L: 99.4 cm; W: 49.8 cm*

Huang Binhong (1864–1955) originally named Zhi, used the sobriquet Pucun and the nicknames Yuxiang,[1] Honglu[2] and Hongsou.[3] His ancestral home was in She County, Anhui, but he was born in Jinhua, Zhejiang. Since childhood he was a diligent student, and at the age of 21 went to Yangzhou to take a position as clerk in the office of the Salt Commissioner. He also began to study landscape painting with Zheng Shan[4] and actively supported the 1911 Revolution. Beginning in 1907, he lived in Shanghai for 30 years, working successively in a newspaper office, a publishing firm and the Academy of Fine Arts. During this period, he did a great deal of traveling and saw the famous mountains and rivers of China. Even though he was old, he never visited a place without sketching it to record its beauty. In 1937 his entire family moved to Beijing, where he served as a professor in the Beijing Training School for the Arts. In the autumn of 1948 he accepted an invitation to teach at the Hangzhou Training School for the Arts, and after the establishment of the People's Republic, went to teach at the East China Branch of the Central Academy of Art, and also served as Vice Chairman of the East China Branch of the Chinese Association of Artists. In 1955 he took sick and died. In accordance with his last wishes, his family donated to the nation all of the more than ten thousand calligraphies and paintings that he had collected in his lifetime and his home was made the Huang Binhong Memorial House.[5]

Huang Binhong matured late as a landscape painter. His early style was deeply influenced by the Xin'an school.[6] After his middle years, however, he saw his fill of the great natural sights, and with the foundation he had acquired in reshaping ancient techniques, began to comprehend the natural interest and charm of real landscapes. His landscapes are boldly free and forceful, vigorous and splendid. He was expert at using simultaneously splattered ink, accumulated ink, aged ink and broken ink. His compositions are carefully structured, and his artistic conceptions reserved. The terms "dark, dense, thick and heavy" best describe his unique style. In addition to landscapes, he also painted birds and flowers and insects which are odd and winsome.

He was a poet, a writer in prose and a calligrapher and

was fascinated by seal cutting in metal and stone. He was also a fine connoisseur and was very well versed in art theory and art history. His publications include *Huangshan Huajia Yuanliu Kao*,[7] *Honglu Huatan*,[8] *Guhua Wei*,[9] *Zhongguo Huaxueshi Dagang*,[10] and *Binhong Caotang Cangyin*.[11] Together with Deng Shi, he edited *Meishu Congshu*.[12]

Done in 1946 when the artist was 83 years old, this painting depicts the mountain scenery of the Jiangnan region with its peaks and cliffs, one rising higher than another, its winding mists and clouds, its mountain paths, along which hamlets appear and disappear. The brushwork is very varied and marvelously unconventional and fully expresses the beauty of the natural world. The composition however is a mixture of the real and unreal. It makes the viewer approach as an intimate relative; there are mountains in all directions and the beautiful scenery invites one to enter and look at the sights. This is a piece which affords the greatest delight.

( 1)  予向 .
( 2)  虹庐 .
( 3)  虹叟 .
( 4)  郑珊 : (?–1869?), a painter of flowers and landscapes.
( 5)  画家黄宾虹纪念室 . In Hangzhou.
( 6)  新安派 . One of the two painting schools flourishing in Anhui, which at the end of the 17th century regarded Ni Zan (1301–1374) as their main inspiration.
( 7)  黄山画家源流考 : *Study on the Origin and Development of the Huangshan Painters.*
( 8)  虹庐画谈 : *Rainbow Hut's Discourses on Painting,* published 1926. See footnote (2) above.
( 9)  古画微 : *Trivia on Ancient Painting,* published 1961.
(10)  中国画学史大纲 : *An Outline History on the Study of Chinese Painting,* compiled 1948.
(11)  宾虹草堂藏印 : *The Binhong Collection of Seals,* published 1929.
(12)  美术丛书 : *Art Series,* 1910–1936.

### 159.  "Old Cypress," Hanging Scroll on Paper
*By Xu Beihong, Modern, dated 1934*
*L:110.0 cm; W: 52.8 cm*

Xu Beihong (1895–1953) was from Yixing, Jiangsu, where he was born into a poor family of common folk. His father was a self-trained painter, and at the age of nine Xu Beihong began to study painting with him. In 1919 he went to study in Paris at the École des Beaux-Arts, returned home in 1927 and served as Dean of the Beijing Academy of Arts. After the establishment of the People's Republic of China in 1949, he was appointed Director of the Central Academy of Fine Arts and at the same time was selected Chairman of the National Association of Art Workers. He died of a stroke in 1953 at the age of 59. His home became the Xu Beihong Memorial Museum.

Xu Beihong consistently opposed formalism and advocated realism. He insisted that with reality as a starting point Chinese painting should "learn its ways from nature." He was opposed to following outmoded rules and was excellent at making well-knit sketches. He assimilated the traditional flavor of Chinese painting, taking advantage of his solid foundation of Western draftsmanship to form a style with distinctive national characteristics. All his life he produced historical paintings with progressive ideas, such as the story of "Jiufang Gao"[1] and "Old Yu Moves the Mountain,"[2] integrating Western realistic techniques into his creative process. He was a skilled animal painter and is particularly appreciated at home and abroad for his paintings of horses. It is because he carried forward the fine traditions of Chinese classical painting while assimilating the beneficial ingredients in Western realism that he gave an impetus to the technical reform of Chinese painting.

Xu Beihong did this painting in 1934 when he was 40. The trunk, branches and bare twigs of this majestic old cypress are outlined with a completely uninhibited brush. The dotted leaves are done in the broken brush technique and given a wash of light ink and indigo, which amply portray the vigorous luxuriance of the old cypress. The effect is fresh and pleasing to the eye.

(1)  九方皋 . Jiufang Gao was a judge of horses who lived in the Warring States period in the state of Qin. Asked by the Duke of Qin to find him the best horse on earth, Jiufang Gao produced a yellow mare. The Duke rejected this choice without seeing the horse in the flesh, but later agreed the mare was indeed the best horse to be found. Jiufang Gao's story became a metaphor for the frustrations of unappreciated men of talent in their efforts to obtain government positions.
(2)  "愚公移山 ." "The Foolish Old Man Who Moved the Mountain" is the story of an old fool who convinced the members of his family to remove a mountain which blocked the view from his house, thus showing that no task is impossible for people with determination.

### 160.  "Bald Vulture," Hanging Scroll on Paper
*By Pan Tianshou, Modern*
*L:152.0 cm; W: 49.7 cm*

Pan Tianshou (1897–1971), originally named Tianshou,[1] used the sobriquet Dayi and signed his name[2] variously as Ashou,[3] Leipotoufengshouzhe[4] and Shouzhe.[5] He was from Ninghai, Zhejiang. He loved to paint even as a child, diligently studied on his own and also received instruction from Li Shutong and Wu Changshuo,[6] painters of the preceding generation. Young as he was, he passed in painting circles as a budding talent. Later on for a long period of time he was engaged in painting and art education and taught successively in the art academies and schools of Shanghai, Hangzhou and Chongqing. After the People's Republic of China was established, he was elected Director of the Zhejiang Academy of Fine Arts, Vice Chairman of the Chinese Association of Artists, Chairman of the Zhejiang branch of the Association and honorary member of the Soviet Academy of Art and Science. He emerged as one of China's outstanding painters and art educators of the period.

Pan Tianshou excelled in freehand paintings of birds and flowers, as well as landscapes. He had thoroughly studied traditional painting techniques, spending a lot of time especially on the styles of Xu Wei,[7] Zhu Da,[8] Shitao[9] and Shixi.[10] In addition, the works of the great contemporaneous painters Wu Changshuo[11] and Qi Baishi[12] exerted considerable influence on him. He picked the best and finest in all of them, while advocating a reform of Chinese painting based on folk traditions. Especially robust and bold, his use of the brush allowed him to achieve remarkable results in landscape and bird-and-flower painting. He would frequently use a huge rock as a framework and then combine it with birds, flowers and plants in perilous and novel arrangements. He was skilled in the use of splashed and "scorched" ink,[13] and his application of colors often creates a sense of classic elegance. Though many of his paintings show commonplace scenes, they make an impression of great vitality and grandeur and are strongly individualized. Pan Tianshou was also good at making finger paintings, which were even more gloomy and bizarre. He was also an accomplished calligrapher and seal carver, a very good poet and was well-versed in the history and theory of painting. He published *A History of Chinese Painting*[14] and *Collected Discussions on Seal Studies*.[15]

This painting of a bald vulture is a finger painting. Pan Tianshou uses bold and vigorous lines to render the hardness of the solid rock, and the bald vulture's beak and hooked claws are depicted with vigor. The vulture's body and wings are covered with soaking wet ink and random nail marks, which make the feathers look few and far between and in total disarray. This is a fine finger painting of his later years.

( 1)  天授.
( 2)  Using the following nicknames.
( 3)  阿寿.
( 4)  雷婆头峰寿者.
( 5)  寿者.
( 6)  See Figure 156.
( 7)  See Figure 103.
( 8)  See Figure 130.
( 9)  See Colorplate XLII.
(10)  Also known as Kuncan. See Figure 129.
(11)  See Figure 156.
(12)  See Colorplate LII.
(13)  See Catalogue no. 130, footnote (16).
(14)  中国绘画史.
(15)  治印谈丛.

### 161.  Basket, Carved Ivory
*Contemporary (1911–     )*
*H: 31.0 cm; D (base): 12.5 cm*

The octagonal ivory basket is carved entirely in openwork. The bow-shaped handle displays floral designs and the basket old men reading and playing chess in a secluded grove. The intricate, refined openwork and the lace-like appearance of the object exemplify the superb technique of the craftsman. This is a product of Guangdong, an area renowned for its openwork ivories.

### 162.  Vase with Carved Birds and Chains, White Jade
*Contemporary (1911–     )*
*H: 14.9 cm; D (mouth): 4.3 cm*

This vase is carved from one piece of jade of superb quality. It has a design of confronting birds and flowers. The two ring handles of the vase and the transverse one are ornamented with animal masks. The lid and ring handles are linked together by a chain made of rings skillfully cut in openwork. Both the shape and decoration of this piece are in keeping with the special flavor of traditional pieces.

### 163.  Double Vase with Carved Dragons, Jadeite
(Colorplate XLIX)
*Contemporary (1911–     )*
*H: 19.6 cm; D: 5.2 cm*

The double vase with connecting cover is carved from an entire piece of *feicui*.[1] Four dragons among clouds appear on each side of the vase, and the base displays a pair of lively carps frolicking in waves. Between the vessels are two dragons fighting for the pearl. Surmounting the lid are *lingzhi* fungus,[2] bats and a large coiled dragon, which forms a group with the ones below. The artist correlated his design to the natural distribution of colors in the piece of jade. Its extremely refined workmanship and glittering openwork make this an outstanding piece among *feicui* jades.

(1)  *Feicui*, a term used to describe brilliant green jadeite from Burma.
(2)  *Lingzhi*: see Catalogue no. 145, footnote (2).

# TABLE OF CORRESPONDENCE Pinyin/Wade-Giles

| Pinyin | Wade-Giles | Pinyin | Wade-Giles | Pinyin | Wade-Giles | Pinyin | Wade-Giles | Pinyin | Wade-Giles |
|---|---|---|---|---|---|---|---|---|---|
| ba | pa | dang | tang | jue | chüeh | qian | ch'ien | xiao | hsiao |
| bai | pai | dao | tao | jun | chün | qiang | ch'iang | xie | hsieh |
| ban | pan | de | te | | | qiao | ch'iao | xin | hsin |
| bang | pang | dei | tei | ka | k'a | qie | ch'ieh | xing | hsing |
| bao | pao | deng | teng | kai | k'ai | qin | ch'in | xiong | hsiung |
| bei | pei | di | ti | kan | k'an | qing | ch'ing | xiu | hsiu |
| ben | pen | dian | tien | kang | k'ang | qiong | ch'iung | xu | hsü |
| beng | peng | diao | tiao | kao | k'ao | qiu | ch'iu | xuan | hsüan |
| bi | pi | die | tieh | ke | k'o | qu | ch'ü | xue | hsüeh |
| bian | pien | ding | ting | ken | k'en | quan | ch'üan | xun | hsün |
| biao | piao | diu | tiu | keng | k'eng | que | ch'üeh | | |
| bie | pieh | dong | tung | kong | k'ung | qun | ch'ün | yan | yen |
| bin | pin | dou | tou | kou | k'ou | | | ye | yeh |
| bing | ping | du | tu | ku | k'u | ran | jan | yong | yung |
| bo | po | duan | tuan | kua | k'ua | rang | jang | you | yu |
| bu | pu | dui | tui | kuai | k'uai | rao | jao | yu | yü |
| | | dun | tun | kuan | k'uan | re | je | yuan | yüan |
| ca | ts'a | duo | to | kuang | k'uang | ren | jen | yue | yüeh |
| cai | ts'ai | | | kui | k'uei | reng | jeng | yun | yün |
| can | ts'an | e | o | kun | k'un | ri | jih | | |
| cang | ts'ang | er | erh | kuo | k'uo | rong | jung | za | tsa |
| cao | ts'ao | | | | | rou | jou | zai | tsai |
| ce | ts'e | ga | ka | lian | lien | ru | ju | zan | tsan |
| cen | ts'en | gai | kai | lie | lieh | ruan | juan | zang | tsang |
| ceng | ts'eng | gan | kan | long | lung | rui | jui | zao | tsao |
| cha | ch'a | gang | kang | luo | lo | run | jun | ze | tse |
| chai | ch'ai | gao | kao | lue | lüeh | ruo | jo | zei | tsei |
| chan | ch'an | ge | ko | | | | | zen | tsen |
| chang | ch'ang | gei | kei | mian | mien | shi | shih | zeng | tseng |
| chao | ch'ao | gen | ken | mie | mieh | si | ssu | zha | cha |
| che | ch'e | geng | keng | | | song | sung | zhai | chai |
| chen | ch'en | gong | kung | nian | nien | suo | so | zhan | chan |
| cheng | ch'eng | gou | kou | nie | nieh | | | zhang | chang |
| chi | ch'ih | gu | ku | nong | nung | ta | t'a | zhao | chao |
| chong | ch'ung | gua | kua | nuo | no | tai | t'ai | zhe | che |
| chou | ch'ou | guai | kuai | nue | nueh | tan | t'an | zhei | chei |
| chu | ch'u | guan | kuan | | | tang | t'ang | zhen | chen |
| chua | ch'ua | guang | kuang | pa | p'a | tao | t'ao | zheng | cheng |
| chuai | ch'uai | gui | kuei | pai | p'ai | te | t'e | zhi | chih |
| chuan | ch'uan | gun | kun | pan | p'an | teng | t'eng | zhong | chung |
| chuang | ch'uang | guo | kuo | pang | p'ang | ti | t'i | zhou | chou |
| chui | ch'ui | | | pao | p'ao | tian | t'ien | zhu | chu |
| chun | ch'un | he | ho | pei | p'ei | tiao | t'iao | zhua | chua |
| chuo | ch'o | hong | hung | pen | p'en | tie | t'ieh | zhuai | chuai |
| ci | tz'u | | | peng | p'eng | ting | t'ing | zhuan | chuan |
| cong | ts'ong | ji | chi | pi | p'i | tong | t'ung | zhuang | chuang |
| cou | ts'ou | jia | chia | pian | p'ien | tou | t'ou | zhui | chui |
| cu | ts'u | jian | chien | piao | p'iao | tu | t'u | zhun | chun |
| cuan | ts'uan | jiang | chiang | pie | p'ieh | tuan | t'uan | zhuo | cho |
| cui | ts'ui | jiao | chiao | pin | p'in | tui | t'ui | zi | tzu |
| cun | ts'un | jie | chieh | ping | p'ing | tun | t'un | zong | tsung |
| cuo | ts'o | jin | chin | po | p'o | tou | t'o | zou | tsou |
| | | jing | ching | pou | p'ou | | | zu | tsu |
| da | ta | jiong | chiung | pu | p'u | xi | hsi | zuan | tsuan |
| dai | tai | jiu | chiu | | | xia | hsia | zui | tsui |
| dan | tan | ju | chü | qi | ch'i | xian | hsien | zun | tsun |
| | | juan | chüan | qia | ch'ia | xiang | hsiang | zuo | tso |

# FURTHER READING

**Ayers, John, and Jessica Rawson.**
*Chinese Jade Throughout the Ages.* London, Oriental Ceramic Society, 1975.

**Cahill, James.**
*Chinese Painting.* New York, Rizzoli International, 1978.

*Parting at the Shore: Chinese Painting of the Early and Middle Ming.* New York and Tokyo, Weatherhill, 1978.

**Chang, Kwang-chih.**
*The Archaeology of Ancient China.* New Haven, Yale University Press, 1977.

*Shang Civilization.* New Haven, Yale University Press, 1980.

**Fong, Wen, editor.**
*The Great Bronze Age of China.* New York, the Metropolitan Museum of Art, 1980.

**Ho Wai-kam,** *et al.*
*Eight Dynasties of Chinese Painting.* Cleveland, Cleveland Museum of Art, 1980.

**Lefebvre d'Argencé, René-Yvon,** *et al.*
*Chinese, Japanese and Korean Sculpture in the Avery Brundage Collection.* San Francisco, Asian Art Museum of San Francisco, 1974.

*Bronze Vessels of Ancient China in the Avery Brundage Collection.* San Francisco, Asian Art Museum of San Francisco, 1977.

*Chinese Jades in the Avery Brundage Collection.* San Francisco, Asian Art Museum of San Francisco, 1977.

**Li, Chu-tsing.**
*Trends in Modern Chinese Painting (The C. A. Drenowatz Collection).* Ascona, Artibus Asiae, 1979. (Artibus Asiae, Supplementum 36.)

**Medley, Margaret.**
*The Chinese Potter.* New York, Scribner, 1976.

**Rawson, Jessica.**
*Ancient China: Art and Archaeology.* New York, Harper and Row, 1980.

**Riddell, Sheila.**
*Dated Chinese Antiquities: 600–1650.* London, Faber and Faber, 1979.

**Satō, Masahiko.**
*Chinese Ceramics: A Short History.* New York and Tokyo, Weatherhill and Heibonsha, 1978.

**Shanghai Museum.**
*Shanghai Bowuguan Cang Hua (Paintings in the Collection of the Shanghai Museum).* Shanghai, Shanghai Bowuguan, 1959.

*Shanghai Bowuguan Cang Qingtongqi (Bronze Vessels in the Collection of the Shanghai Museum).* Shanghai, Shanghai Bowuguan, 1964.

*Songren Huace (Album Paintings by Song Artists).* Shanghai, Shanghai Bowuguan, 1979.

*Shanghai Bowuguan Cang Ci Xuanji (A Selection of Ceramics in the Collection of the Shanghai Museum).* Beijing, Wen Wu Publishing Company, 1979.

*Shanghai Hakubutsukan Chinzō Bumbutsu Ten (Exhibition of Ancient Cultural Properties of the Shanghai Museum).* Yokohama, 1980.

**Sullivan, Michael.**
*Arts of China.* Berkeley and Los Angeles, University of California Press, 1979.

*Symbols of Eternity: The Art of Landscape Painting in China.* Stanford, Stanford University Press, 1979.

**Watt, James C. Y.**
*Jades from Han to Ch'ing.* New York, Asia Society and John Weatherhill Inc., 1980.